A Nurse Called Tommy

Author
Norman, Thelma   P.B.
                        Copy 21

1—N

A Nurse Called Tommie

A Nurse Called

Tommie

by Thelma Giddings Norman

PACIFIC PRESS PUBLISHING ASSOCIATION
Mountain View, California
Omaha, Nebraska   Oshawa, Ontario

Contents

Sequel to
"A Girl Called Tommie"

Tommie Keeps the Sabbath | 1

Tommie Gordon hurried to greet her parents after the excitement of her eighth-grade graduation.

"I'm beginning to feel grown-up already," she announced.

"You still have some growing to do, young lady," her mother laughed; "but you'll probably look back on these days as some of the happiest in your life."

"I'm sure you're right, Mamma," said Tommie thoughtfully. "I've had a wonderful life here in the Ozark Mountains. Bud, Becky Jane, Bill, and I have been lucky children to live on a farm and spend so much time outdoors."

"You've had to work hard, but you've had fun too." Then her mother remembered something. "Just think, Tommie, one of your nicest graduation presents is still ahead of you!"

"That's right! I'm going to visit Aunt Marty and Cousin Delores. What fun!" Tommie's eyes sparkled in anticipation, and she was especially intrigued because her aunt and cousin were Seventh-day Adventists.

During the next two weeks Tommie did some serious thinking. For nearly a year she had been studying the Adventist beliefs, and the time had come for her to make a decision. She could either accept the things she had been reading and begin to live them, or she could try to forget them. She knew it would not be an easy decision, but it had to be made. Her father's attitude toward Adventists was a further complication.

He told her repeatedly that Adventists were all liars, that they preached one thing and lived another, and that he wanted none of his family to be mixed up in anything like that. Tommie decided to wait until after her visit to Aunt Marty's before making up her mind. Surely during the visit she would find out whether her father was right about the Adventist people.

Finally the day came for Tommie to be on her way with Aunt Nola. She was full of questions she hoped would be answered before she returned home. This was to be her first visit in the home of her Adventist relatives, and she planned to listen and watch carefully and not miss a thing.

It was a happy, wonderful week. Tommie and Delores went on picnics, swam, played games, and talked girl-talk. Every evening they studied the Sabbath School lesson. When Friday came, everyone helped get ready for the Sabbath. The house was cleaned, Sabbath clothes were made ready, Sabbath dinner was cooked, and nothing was left undone when it was time for evening worship.

Adventists have a special look when the sun goes down on Friday evening, Tommie decided. It would be wonderful to look forward to Sabbath every week.

Sabbath School was all Tommie had hoped it would be. She loved the music, sat enthralled by the mission story, and knew the answer to every question during the class discussion, although she was too shy to answer aloud.

During the church service she sat quietly, surprised at how much she understood from her own Bible study. After church the congregation stood outside and talked. Tommie thought she had never met such warm, friendly people. Surely Daddy must be wrong about them.

There was a Missionary Volunteer program that afternoon. Tommie enjoyed every minute of the day, right down to sundown worship. She had kept her first Sabbath, but she decided that it was not the last Sabbath she was going to keep!

A quiet girl rode back with Aunt Nola the next day. There was too much to think about to allow much time for talk. Tommie had made her decision: She was going to be a Seventh-day Adventist, not in some distant future, but right then. How the details were going to be worked out she didn't know. She felt that it was not going to be easy.

That night she knelt by her bed to pray, something she had learned to do in the past week. In bed, she tried to sleep, but her thoughts kept going around and around. "I am going to be a Seventh-day Adventist. I have to. There isn't any other way. But I don't know how I'm going to manage it. There aren't any other Adventists around here, and I have no idea where the nearest Adventist church is. Even if I did know, I'd have no way to get there, and besides,

Daddy would never give me permission to go. What will he say about it all, anyway? He dislikes Adventists so. I know he won't let me keep the Sabbath, and I don't see how I can; only I must, and I am going to somehow. With the Lord's help I can." With that thought she finally went to sleep.

The next morning Tommie's mother realized something was different. Tommie was tense and unlike her usual cheerful self. Finally, after careful questioning, Mamma got to the fact that Tommie intended to be a Sabbath keeper. Mamma cried awhile and pleaded with Tommie to change her mind, reminding her of her father's attitude toward Seventh-day Adventists. Tommie stood firm. She knew her mother would soon adjust to the idea and might possibly help her. It was breaking the news to Daddy that worried Tommie most.

That evening she waited until she caught her father alone in the living room. She approached him fearfully as he sat reading.

"Daddy," she began haltingly.

He lowered the paper and frowned slightly. "Well, what is it?"

Her words were rushed, lest her scant supply of courage give way, "Dad, I want to be a Seventh-day Adventist!"

"Well," he answered, "you may be."

Tommie went limp with gratitude and relief. Then her father continued angrily: "But not as long as you live in my house. Until you are twenty-one you will be under my care, and you're not going to be a Seventh-day Adventist! Is that clear? Nola put you up to this when you were visiting there last week, and you don't even know what it means."

"But, Daddy, she didn't," protested Tommie. "She doesn't even know—"

Her father interrupted harshly, "Be quiet! I know she did. Your aunts have always wanted you to join that church, and you don't even know what you are getting into. Let me tell you, you are going to work on Saturday just like the rest of us. Do you understand?"

"Yes, Daddy," Tommie whispered as she left the room. Her father always demanded instant, unquestioning obedience from his children, and never before had one defied him once his wishes were made plain.

Tommie huddled miserably on her bed. "Lord," she whispered, "I don't know how I'm going to do it, but I'm going to keep this Sab-

3

bath. Please help me." After that she felt better and joined the rest of the family doing the evening chores.

On Friday Tommie's duties kept her at the house, and she spent the morning trembling with fear. She had determined to tell her father at noon that she couldn't possibly wait until she was twenty-one to be an Adventist. She had to be a Sabbath keeper from that day on because the Lord required it of her. She didn't know what would happen when she told him. She was sure it would be unpleasant.

Tommie became more and more frightened as noon approached. At last she knelt and prayed a nearly incoherent prayer for help and strength to meet the ordeal ahead. Suddenly her fear left, and she was filled with peace. She wondered if the Lord had sent an angel to be with her. For a moment she dared not open her eyes, lest she see the angel there beside her. With a heart full of love and gratitude she murmured, "Thank You, Lord! Thank You so much!"

She went up the path to meet her father as he came in for his noon meal, wanting to spare the rest of the family the scene that was sure to follow. With a calmness she wouldn't have believed possible an hour before, she explained to him that the Lord meant so much to her that it was necessary to obey Him now. It would be wrong to wait six years before becoming one of His people.

Her father became angry, demanding that she give up any such ideas, and threatening to punish her severely if she didn't. Tommie did not argue, but her heart was serene in the knowledge that, come what might, she was going to obey the Lord. She knew He would help her as He had in the hour just past.

The next morning after breakfast, while her father was hitching up the team, Tommie gathered together the torn remnants of the Bible, the hymnal, *The Desire of Ages,* and the latest copy of the *Instructor,* and slipped out of the house. She was determined to keep this Sabbath!

She made her way up the hill above the house, crept into an old storage shed, and hid behind some bales of hay. The habit of obedience to her father was so strong that she started violently when she heard him call her. Then she shrank back behind the hay and hoped that the thundering of her heart would not give her away if he came near looking for her. After a few minutes of calling, her father and the rest of the family went on to the fields. Then Tommie crept from her hiding place.

4

She sat on a log to hold her own Sabbath School, trying to remember how the program had gone the week before at Aunt Marty's church. It was noon almost before she knew it, and she went into hiding again when the family came home to eat. After they had gone back, she went down to the kitchen to find some food and then went back to the old shed. She spent the afternoon in study and prayer.

After sunset she went down to the house, ready for whatever punishment would be given her. Her father greeted her furiously, as she had been sure he would.

"Now, look here, young lady; you listen to me! You just once more try the trick you pulled today, and I'll use my razor strop on you until you won't be able to run and hide again! I mean it! I won't punish you this time, for it is just possible you did not realize the seriousness of what you were doing; but next time you will have no excuse, so there had better not be a next time!"

Tommie knew better than to answer back, but her silence seemed to make her father angrier. He continued, "Until you get over this foolishness, you are not to consider yourself one of the family, understand? You are to stay here, of course, as I am your guardian until you are twenty-one, but you are not to eat with us or be called a member of the family. Now, is that clear?"

Tommie understood. It was clear. Yet she felt it was a small price to pay for being able to keep the Sabbath. Only—next Sabbath the price promised to be higher. Would she have the courage to pay it? She knew her father did not deal out threats lightly. She could not remember a time he had not carried out any threat he had made.

The week went by, and Tommie alternated between the happiness she had found in obeying the Lord and the dread of the punishment that was sure to be hers when the next Sabbath was over. In fact, she was not at all sure she would have the courage to disobey her father when the time came.

She ate her meals when the rest of the family had finished eating, and was avoided with awe by her younger brothers and sister. She knew her mother shed tears over the situation. They had all been so accustomed to doing just as her father said that none of them dared ask him to be more lenient with Tommie.

The next Sabbath morning Tommie again found courage to hide away in the storage shed and keep the Sabbath. Before she left to go back to the house at sunset she prayed for a long time, asking the

5

Lord to help her meet her punishment in such a way that when it was over she would still have the courage to go on doing the right thing.

Her father met her at the door, his voice trembling with anger as he shouted, "Don't you remember I told you never to slip away to follow your own religion until you are of age to leave home? You are going to find yourself in serious trouble. Don't ever do it again, or I will give you a beating you will never forget. Now, go and help with the evening chores, and remember what I have just told you, or you'll be mighty sorry!"

Succeeding Sabbaths followed the same pattern. Tommie would slip away and hide early in the morning, and when she returned at night she would be met with harsh words and threats. But the threats were not carried out.

On weekdays her father subjected her to ridicule and criticism. She submitted to this in silence. To answer back or try to explain would have made matters worse. Sabbath became more and more a day of strength and peace for her. The serenity she found during its sacred hours carried her through each difficult week, and no price seemed too high to pay for the blessings she received.

Links in the Chain | 2

Another school year was almost over. The first flowers of early spring were spotting the hills, although the air was still crisp on early mornings and late afternoons.

Tommie put the finishing touches on the little basket she was weaving and held it up for Mamma to see.

"This isn't too bad for a first try, is it, Mamma?" she asked.

"Fishing for compliments, aren't you?" smiled Mamma. "Very well, I'll oblige. Yes, its a very nice basket for a beginner. What have you decided to do with it?"

"I want to put a plant in it and give it to Mrs. Hedges," replied Tommie. "Do you think that would be all right?"

"Of course," said Mamma. "I think she'd like it very much."

"She loves wild flowers, but she seldom has time to drive out after any; she's so busy teaching. She's the best teacher I ever had," declared Tommie.

Mamma smiled at Tommie's enthusiasm, but nodded agreement. "Yes, she's a fine person and a wonderful teacher. Why, we never knew we had an artist in the family until she started bringing out your talent!"

"Oh, Mamma, I'm not—not an artist!" Tommie quickly denied. "Not yet, anyway. But I do hope to be someday. Maybe I can illustrate children's books, or something like that. We'll have to wait and see if I'm good enough at art to do anything with it. I'm just learning now."

"Mrs. Hedges is very pleased with what you've done so far," said Mamma. "She spoke to me about it at the last PTA meeting and showed me some of your work. She was especially proud of your charcoal sketches."

"Well, this little basket is to show my appreciation for the help she's given me," said Tommie.

7

"Have you decided what kind of plant you're going to put in the basket, Tommie?" asked Mamma.

"I saw some hepaticas yesterday over by the ridge road," Tommie replied. "If I line the basket with moss, the green side facing out, one or two hepatica plants would just about fill it. I'll have to hurry, though, if I'm going to have it ready to take to her tomorrow."

"All right, then. Run along," said Mamma. "You can bring in the cows on the way back."

Tommie took an old kitchen knife and a small box for the moss and plants and walked quickly to the barn. Crossing the barn lot, she entered the woods beyond and climbed the first hill. The hepaticas she had seen were in the small depression on the other side of the hill.

The lovely blue flowers were surrounded by three-lobed leaves that had a faint reddish-brown edging. Tommie found two plants whose flowers were darker than the others. She dug carefully with the knife and gently pulled away the stones until each plant was free with a big clump of dirt clinging to its roots.

Tommie noticed that the knife had worn and broken a blister in the palm of her right hand. "I'll have to be sure to wash that when I get home," she said to herself. "I wouldn't want to get an infection. First, though, I need to get some moss and then find the cows."

It took only a few minutes to find the moss she needed, and after gathering it and placing it in the box, Tommie stood listening for cowbells. Yes, there came the tinkling of a bell. It sounded as if the cows were farther up the ridge road. When the cows saw Tommie coming, they knew why she was there and they started slowly toward the barn, Tommie trailing them.

When they came to the creek, Tommie went across on the stepping-stones, carefully balancing her box of plants as she did so. She grinned as she thought how, a year ago, she would have ignored the stepping-stones entirely and would have crossed the creek triumphantly astride the back of one of the cows. Now that she was a freshman in high school she had to be more dignified, and that eliminated such things as riding cows and catching snakes. Such was the price of growing up.

Shutting the cows inside the barn lot, Tommie went to the house to finish the gift for Mrs. Hedges. Tommie's sister, Becky, watched as Tommie lined the basket with moss and arranged the plants in it. When it was finished, both girls looked at it happily. It was a colorful sight, the yellow of the basket setting off the green of the moss and the whole crowned with the hepatica flowers rising above their leaves.

"Oh-h-h, how pretty," breathed Becky. She added wistfully, "My teacher likes pretty things too. Do you suppose you could help me make one for her, Tommie?"

"I think so," replied Tommie, "but we can't do it tonight. I have to help milk the cows. I know. You gather the material for the basket and put it to soak tonight, and tomorrow we can start your basket!"

"All right," Becky agreed and skipped happily away as Tommie went to get the milk buckets.

The next morning Tommie noticed her hand was stiff, but she decided it was just from digging the plants the day before. She took her basket with its plants to school and forgot her stiff hand.

"Oh, Tommie, how beautiful," exclaimed Mrs. Hedges with delight when Tommie gave her the gift. "I'd rather have this than anything you could buy at the florist."

"I enjoyed making it for you," Tommie said shyly.

"I've noticed that you enjoy making things," said Mrs. Hedges, "and I've been thinking—do you think you might be interested in interior decorating when you finish high school?"

"Why, I—I don't know," replied Tommie. "Up until this year I had thought only of teaching. Now I don't know— I like art so much better. But there won't be money for college, anyway, unless I can get a scholarship."

"If you continue in your art work as you have this year, you can easily get a scholarship to a school of art and design," Mrs. Hedges reassured her. "I wish you'd think about it and work toward that end. I know you are young and have three more years of high school, but you'll find they will go by faster if you have a definite goal in mind."

"I'll think about it," promised Tommie as she left for her first class.

During the day Tommie was aware of a nagging little ache in her right hand. It intruded now and then through her concentration on her lessons. When Tommie arrived home from school, Mamma had her soak the hand in kerosene and excused her from helping with the milking that night. The hand was beginning to swell, and there were a few red streaks running up her wrist from the palm of the hand.

Tommie slept fitfully that night, for the pain in her hand was worse. The next morning Daddy inspected the swollen, red hand. "We'll have to let the doctor see this, Tommie," he said.

Ordinarily Tommie enjoyed the long slow trip in the wagon the five miles to town where the doctor had his office, but today she did not. Her hand throbbed, and she felt sick all over. Besides, she was worried about the visit to the doctor. She had never been to the doctor before, and she had a feeling that whatever he did to her hand would be unpleasant, probably painful.

Dr. France examined the hand, quickly opened and drained the abscess in the palm, and applied ointment to it. As he bandaged it he said to Daddy, "An abscess in the palm of the hand can be a pretty dangerous thing. I want to see this and redress it every day for at least a week. Can you bring her back every day?"

"I'll have to leave her in town with her grandparents," replied Daddy. "They live about two blocks down the street, and her grandmother can send Tommie in every day."

"Fine," approved the doctor. "Just so she's here every day."

Granny and Grandpa were very happy to have Tommie come to spend a week with them. They had only recently moved into town from Uncle Bill's farm, and they missed being close to the rest of the family. Daddy came the next day with Tommie's clothes and some of her school books so she wouldn't get too far behind in her lessons. He didn't stay long, for this was one of the busiest seasons on the farm.

"I'm glad you're here so you can go to church with us tonight, Tommie," said Grandpa almost a week later. "We have a wonderful minister. You'll like him."

Granny and Grandpa carefully refrained from making any remarks about Tommie's Adventist beliefs. When she had tried to explain what she believed and why, they always managed to change the subject.

When they reached the church that night, Grandpa engaged the minister in earnest conversation while Granny introduced Tommie to some of the young people of the congregation. After prayer and a song service the minister stood up to speak.

"I know," he said, "that you came here expecting to hear a sermon entitled 'Where Are the Dead?' as was announced last week. However, I am going to postpone that sermon until next week. Tonight I am going to speak on 'The Ten Commandments.' "

"Oh, good," thought Tommie. "I should be able to understand part of that."

Suddenly a loud voice ripped through her thoughts. "The Ten Commandments? Why, Preacher, surely we don't have to worry about them anymore!" came the voice from the back of the room.

Tommie started and looked around. Who was so rude as to make such an outcry right in church? The lady next to her looked at her and smiled, and Grandpa leaned over to whisper, "Our minister used to be a ventriloquist in a circus, Tommie. He is throwing his own voice to the back of the room!"

The minister went on with his sermon and Tommie grew confused. He said the Ten Commandments had been done away with, particularly the one pertaining to the Sabbath. He said that the Sabbath had been changed to Sunday. He said a great many things, and quoted the Bible in a way that seemed to prove he was right.

Finally the sermon was over. The minister came and shook her hand, and asked, "Well, young lady, what did you think of that sermon?"

"Why," thought Tommie in amazement, "he preached that sermon just because of me! He knows I'm an Adventist. Grandpa must have told him!"

Aloud she said, "I don't know. I'll have to think about it!"

"You do that," he said with a satisfied air. "If you think about it, you'll come to believe I'm right."

Tommie went to bed with her mind in a whirl. Suppose that minister was right! Had she been defying her father over a Sabbath that no longer mattered? What should she believe? Surely the Lord wouldn't make a set of rules and then just throw them away! Was she wrong? No, she decided, the Lord had led her every step of the way so far. He wouldn't have led her the wrong way. And besides, she remembered with astonishment, even Daddy never tried to tell her the Adventists were wrong—he only said they didn't practice what they preached. Somewhere there was an explanation. Aunt Nola would know. Tommy decided to write to her the next day and tell her the problem. She was glad her hand was well enough so she could write again.

Tommie wrote the letter early the next morning and sent it to Aunt Nola. Aunt Nola, Aunt Marty, and Delores had moved to a small Southern town and were working in an Adventist hospital there. Tommie hoped Aunt Nola would have time to answer her questions right away. She mailed the letter as she went for her final visit to the doctor. Her hand was almost completely well now, and Daddy was coming to take her home that day.

With a week of schoolwork to make up, Tommie had little time to be impatient as she waited for an answer to her letter. She used every spare moment for study. After all, final exams were less than three weeks away. But the letter came, and Tommie gladly read the explanations to her problems. No, the Sabbath had not been changed. The Ten Commandments were still in force. Aunt Nola seemed to understand all about the situation. Her letter concluded, "And Tommie, we've written your daddy asking if you can come and spend the summer with us. You can get a job here in the hospital as a nurse's aide, and you will have a chance to learn more about the Adventist faith."

Oh, if she could only go! She went to find Mamma. "Mamma, you know Aunt Nola wants me to spend the summer with her—" she began.

"Yes, I know," said Mamma. "I read the letter she sent Daddy."

"Well, Mamma, do you think he will let me go?" Tommie asked tensely.

"No, Tommie; I doubt it," replied Mamma. "Now don't go getting your hopes up. You'll only be disappointed."

When Daddy came in from milking, he called Tommie into the living room. "Nola wants you to spend the summer with her, Tommie," he said. "Well, I'm going to leave the decision up to you. Just remember one thing: I do not want you to go! Think about it a little while, and let me know what you decide."

"I've already thought about it," said Tommie. "I want to go, please, Daddy!"

"All right," he answered shortly. "We'll consider it settled, then. You'll go as soon as school is out!" He picked up the newspaper and began reading. Tommie could tell he was angry, but he said nothing more.

As Tommie gathered up her school books and went to study, she remembered something she'd read shortly before in one of Grandma's Adventist books—or else the *Youth's Instructor,* she didn't remember which. It was something about "if you live up to the light the Lord has given you, He will lead you into more and more light." "I think that is how it is working out for me," she thought happily.

Tommie Goes Away | 3

Now that it was decided that Tommie would spend the summer with her aunts and cousin in Brownsburg, preparations began. The catalog was taken down from the shelf, and Mamma and Tommie spent a long time deciding on the three dresses to order for Tommie. Usually Mamma made Tommie's dresses, but now the time was short, so they were ordering the dresses ready-made.

The days rushed by. School ended, and soon it would be time for Tommie to leave. The nearer the time came, the more misgivings Tommie had. She knew she would miss her parents and brothers and sister. She'd never been away from home more than a week at a time before. Would she get terribly homesick before the summer was over? Suppose she found that being around sick people bothered her so much she couldn't work in the hospital? Finally she told herself firmly that whatever came, the Lord would see her through. After all, it was His leading that was taking her away from home for the summer.

Finally the day arrived. Uncle Bill came in his car to take them the twenty-five miles to the town where Tommie was to board the train. During the ride nobody seemed to find anything to say. Even Becky Jane was quiet.

When they reached the depot, Daddy went to buy the ticket. He brought it back to Tommie, along with a paper telling where and when she'd change trains, and when she'd arrive in Brownsburg, two days later. She had two waits of several hours each. When she saw that, she was happy that she'd brought several books with her.

"Now, Tommie, above all, you must not lose this ticket," Daddy impressed upon her.

"I won't, Daddy. I'll be very careful," Tommie promised.

Daddy nodded but said no more. He stood with his hands in his pockets, looking off into the distance and whistling softly to himself as he often did when he was preoccupied. Tommie wondered if he regretted letting her decide for herself to make the trip. Was he perhaps thinking of even now forbidding her to go? For a moment Tommie almost hoped he would. Then she thought, "No, I have to leave home sometime. And how am I going to learn to be a good Seventh-day Adventist if I don't take advantage of each opportunity offered me?"

Mamma was upset about Tommie's leaving. She had tried not to let it show, but now, with the time so near, she was no longer able to hide it.

"I don't know, Tommie—" she began doubtfully and then paused, and asked abruptly, "Are you sure you have your ticket, Tommie?"

"Yes, Mamma, it's in my purse," answered Tommie.

"Tommie, remember what I told you about not talking to strangers," Mamma said a little later.

"I'll remember, Mamma," Tommie tried to reassure her.

Mamma was silent for a few moments, running her fingers nervously through her thick black hair.

"Tommie, be sure to eat on this trip. It wouldn't do for you to get so excited that you forgot to eat and made yourself sick even before you got there!"

"All right, Mamma. I'll eat," replied Tommie.

"Are you sure you have enough money, Tommie?" Mamma asked again.

"Oh, yes," said Tommie. "I have all the money I've saved, and Daddy gave me several dollars this morning, and Uncle Bill gave me five dollars when we got here. I have plenty."

Uncle Bill had been standing silent, listening. Now he spoke to Tommie's mother. "Don't worry about Peanuts, Sis," he said. "She'll get there all right!"

"But, Bill, she's so young, and she's never been on a train before or away from home—" began Mamma distractedly.

"Peanuts is smart enough to ride on a train," he said with a wink at Tommie. "That doesn't take a college education."

Tommie was relieved when the train pulled into the station. Good-byes were hurriedly said and Tommie climbed aboard and settled herself by a window so she could wave to the family as the train pulled out. It was hard to hold back the tears, but she had been taught from early childhood that tears were for emergency use only; and this wasn't a real emergency. This was only good-bye for a short while—only three months. She swallowed hard a few times and sat back. There was nothing to do now but enjoy the ride.

That evening Tommie had to make a change, and she read to pass away the hours between trains. Early the next morning she changed trains again. She had tried to obey Mamma and eat, but somehow the sandwiches she bought tasted dry, and the milk she ordered didn't taste like the milk at home, fresh and cold from being set in the spring to cool.

The coach she was riding in was not crowded, and Tommie had the seat to herself. About noon the door opened, and a man in army uniform entered. He looked about, then took the vacant seat next to Tommie.

"Hello there! How are you?" he asked.

"I'm—I'm fine," Tommie answered. "Oh, dear, what shall I do?" she thought to herself. "Mamma told me not to talk to strangers, and I think she meant strange men in particular."

Almost as if reading her thoughts he said with a smile, "I'll bet your mother told you not to talk to strangers, didn't she?"

"Ye—yes," stammered Tommie.

He took a billfold from his pocket and said solemnly, "I'll remedy that. See, here are my identification papers and driver's license. My name is Jeff Anderson, I'm thirty-seven years old, and I have a daughter about your age. Now I'm not a stranger anymore, am I?"

"No," laughed Tommie. "My name is Tommie Gordon, and I'm almost sixteen years old."

"You know, Tommie," said her new friend, "it is really refreshing to meet a young girl whose face isn't covered with paint and lipstick. That's why I took this seat. I'm curious. Tell me, are you a Christian?"

"Yes," declared Tommie unhesitatingly.

"I thought so," he continued. "I'm a chaplain in the Army. I was pastor of a church before I entered the service. What church do you belong to?"

"I'm studying to be a Seventh-day Adventist," Tommie answered.

"I should have known that," Mr. Anderson said. "I know a lot of Adventists and what they believe. They are fine people."

Tommie smiled her appreciation of this compliment to her church. Soon she found herself telling Mr. Anderson all about herself and her family, and in return hearing about him and his family. Time passed swiftly. Several hours later as the train slowed down in a

15

small town, Mr. Anderson stood up and offered Tommie his hand.

"Good-bye, Tommie. Here is where I get off. I have a weekend to spend with my family. See," he pointed through the window, "there's my wife and daughter."

Tommie watched him as he left the train, and saw the pretty teen-age girl enthusiastically hugging her father. He said something to her, then they both turned, smiling, and waved to Tommie as the train slowly moved on.

The train was due in Brownsburg at 7:15 the next morning. Tommie slept soundly most of the night. As she awakened the next morning, the conductor came through the car and smiled at her. "We're right on time," he told her. "We'll be in Brownsburg in a little over an hour."

Tommie stretched and yawned. It would be good to leave the train. A sudden thought struck her—there would be no one to meet her when the train got to Brownsburg! She herself hadn't known until just before she got on the train when she would arrive. For a moment she was frightened; then she thought to herself, "There's nothing to be frightened of! I'll—I'll just get a taxi and go right to Aunt Marty's house." She never thought of telephoning, for never in her life had she used a telephone. Even the taxi was a brave thought, because Tommie had never even seen one, much less ridden in one.

When the train pulled into the Brownsburg station, the first person Tommie saw was Aunt Marty waiting for her.

"How did you know when I would arrive?" was Tommie's question when the first flurry of greetings was over.

"Your daddy sent me a telegram," explained Aunt Marty, "so I took the morning off to meet you and get you acquainted with the hospital and some of the workers before you go to work tomorrow. Right now, though, let's go back to the house. I brought your break-fast down after I ate this morning—we eat all our meals at the hospital cafeteria. Are you hungry?"

Suddenly Tommie felt ravenous. "I surely am," she replied. "I feel as if I haven't eaten for a week."

Later at Aunt Marty's house, having finished off a tray of scram-bled eggs, toast and jelly, canned peaches, and milk, Tommie sat back contentedly. "Now I'm ready for anything," she announced.

"First," said Aunt Marty, "we'll go back to town and buy you some white oxfords to wear with your uniform. The stores weren't open when you got here, or we'd have bought them then."

That errand was soon accomplished. Leaving their purchases at the house, Tommie and her aunt started out. The hospital was at the top of a hill about three blocks from Aunt Marty's house. As they came to the steps that served as a shortcut up to the hospital buildings, Tommie stopped with a gasp of pleasure. The hillside was a mass of flowers, cleverly planted around the large rocks that cropped out in various places.

"I thought you'd like Miss Ruby's rock garden," smiled Aunt Marty, who had seen Tommie's reaction. "Miss Ruby is in charge of the hospital records, and this garden is a hobby of hers. She'll be glad to meet someone who shares her love for flowers. Now," she went on, "this building to your left at the bottom of the hill is the girls' dormitory. The student nurses and most of the nurse's aides have rooms here."

At the top of the hill Aunt Marty paused. "I guess our first stop should be the laundry," she decided.

"The laundry?" questioned Tommie.

"We'll have to fit you out with uniforms," said Aunt Marty, "and that is done at the laundry. Likely there will be some that will fit you, but if they do need any alteration it will have to be done today."

Two uniforms were found that fit perfectly except for length. The seamstress promised to have them shortened and ready to be picked up by five o'clock that afternoon.

As they stood outside the laundry, Aunt Marty continued, "As you can see, there are two main buildings; one is the hospital where we take care of the medical and surgical cases, the more acutely ill patients, and the other building is the sanitarium for people with nervous disorders and less serious ailments. Right now we'll go through the hospital, because that is where you'll be working. I work in the sanitarium most of the time."

"Where is Aunt Nola working?" asked Tommie.

"She works at the switchboard," replied Aunt Marty. "We'll see her in a minute. Delores works in surgery."

As they went through the hospital, Aunt Marty pointed out and explained the functions of the various departments, stopping now and then to introduce Tommie to the hospital workers. "You will notice, Tommie," she said, "that the student nurses wear the light-blue uniforms with white collars and cuffs and a black tie. The graduate nurses wear white, and the aides wear gray."

They paused at the switchboard, but Aunt Nola was so busy

17

that there was only time for a brief word or two, so they went on.

"What do the nurse's aides do, Aunt Marty?" asked Tommie.

"They run errands, give baths, deliver trays at mealtimes, and in general help the nurses. It isn't difficult," her aunt replied. "Wait—here's a girl I want you to meet." Aunt Marty stopped a tall girl in the gray uniform of an aide as she hurried down the hall. "Mollie, I want you to meet my niece, Tommie Gordon. Tommie, this is Mollie Rankin, our head nurse's aide."

"Hey, Tommie! I'm glad to meet you," said Mollie with a pleasant smile. "Are you going to be one of our nurse's aides this summer?"

"I'm starting to work tomorrow," replied Tommie.

"Good!" beamed Mollie. "I'll see you here then!" She hurried away.

"Sometime tomorrow Mollie will teach you how to bathe a bed patient," Aunt Marty said. "Whenever you have any questions, she will be glad to help you."

"I've met so many people today," sighed Tommie. "Anne and Jeannie and Phyllis and Mollie—oh, so many. I'll never be able to keep them all straight in my mind."

"You don't have to do it all in one day," Aunt Marty said reassuringly, "anymore than you have to learn all about your job the first day. It will take time, and everyone will help you learn." She looked at her watch. "I have to go on duty in an hour. That will just give me time to change into my uniform and then have lunch."

"One thing has puzzled me all morning," Tommie said as they stepped outside the hospital after lunch.

"What's that, Tommie?"

"Well, whenever I was introduced to any of the girls, instead of saying 'Hello!' they always said 'Hey!' Does it mean the same thing?"

Aunt Marty chuckled. "It seems to," she replied. "Didn't you notice that Delores said that to you when we saw her in surgery this morning? You'll be saying it, too, before long. It's just a Southern expression." She glanced again at her watch. "I have to go to work soon, and Nola and Delores will not be off duty for over an hour. I hate for you to be left alone to get homesick the very first day." Before Tommie could protest that she wasn't about to be homesick, Aunt Marty exclaimed, "I know—I think Janet is off duty now. Maybe she will walk down to the house with you and the two of you can get acquainted. Wait here—I'll be back in just a minute."

Aunt Marty was soon back with a girl about Tommie's age. She was dressed in the gray uniform too. She was a very pretty girl with

18

long blond hair, expressive blue eyes, and dimples that flashed and twinkled whenever she smiled, which was frequently.

"Janet, this is my niece, Tommie Gordon. Tommie, this is Janet Shafer. She will walk home with you," said Aunt Marty.

"Hey, Tommie," said Janet, her dimples flashing.

"Hey, Janet," replied Tommie with a sly look at Aunt Marty.

Aunt Marty chuckled. "I'll see you tonight at supper, Tommie," she called back as she went on to the sanitarium building to work.

Janet's bubbling personality and spontaneous friendship were irresistible, and within minutes the two girls were chattering like old friends. Tommie was full of questions about Janet's work as an aide, questions Janet answered in detail and with a great deal of humor.

Most of the girls, Janet explained, were academy students who worked as nurse's aides during the summer vacation. Some of the girls were back for their second or third summer.

"How many summers have you been a nurse's aide, Janet?" Tommie asked.

Janet threw back her head and laughed delightedly. "Summers?" she asked. "Why, Tommie, I only started work here a week ago yesterday!"

"You—you did!" exclaimed Tommie in great surprise. "You mean you learned all that in just a week?"

"Of course, Tommie, and so will you," declared Janet. "You just wait and see. We all help each other learn, and you won't be asked to do anything until you've been taught how to do it."

Tommie was doubtful, but Janet proved to be right. When the week was over, Tommie found herself working as self-confidently as if she'd been doing it for years, and enjoying it thoroughly.

Pride Goeth— | 4

"There, now," said Tommie with a smile as she smoothed the last wrinkle from the bedspread. "You look all comfortable and ready for visitors. Is there anything else you'd like, Teddy?"

"Nope, nothin' a'tall," came the answer from the small boy who was the last patient on Tommie's list for that afternoon. "Course you know, nurse, that this here bedspread ain't gonna stay smooth for very long," he continued with a twinkle.

Tommie smothered a smile and said with mock seriousness, "Well, would you mind waiting until I'm gone before you get it all wrinkled? Else I'll feel duty bound to keep smoothing it and make it look right, you know."

He broke out into a mischievous grin. "Then you'd better leave in a hurry," he said, " 'cause I'm just itchin' to turn over. I never could keep still very long!"

Tommie nodded, thinking of the many times that day she'd smoothed the wrinkles this energetic little body had pleated into the sheets, and the many times she'd redone the surgical binder across his thin little middle where his appendix had been removed. "I seem to remember something of the sort," she laughed. "Now be a good boy until I see you on Sunday!"

At the nurses' station Tommie found Janet checking off her final duties. "Are you all through, Tommie?" she asked.

"All through," Tommie replied, "but I'll have to check everything off the book."

"All right, then, hurry, and we can walk to the dormitory together. You don't have to go straight home, do you, Tommie?"

"No, I don't have to go home right way," Tommie answered. "Aunt Marty and Delores won't be through work for another hour or so."

"Good!" exclaimed Janet. "Then we can visit for a while."

20

Tommie checked off her assigned tasks in the workbook, washed her hands, and was ready to go. As the girls left the hospital, Tommie took a deep breath of the hot August air. Someday, perhaps, she'd get used to the smell of the hospital—a smell made up of antiseptics, food, medicine, people, steam, and innumerable other things—but just then she liked the outside atmosphere better.

Janet took her arm as they went down the hill. "Hasn't this been a day!" she sighed. "We didn't get to go to lunch together, and we were kept so busy we hardly had time to say 'Hey' when we met in the hall!"

"I know," agreed Tommie. "I don't know when I've been busier. How did everything go with you?"

"Oh, fine, even if we were busy," replied Janet. "By the way, I noticed you had Teddy on your list today. How is the little rascal? He was on my list yesterday."

"He's fine." Tommie smiled in remembrance. "He warned me that he was going to get the bedspread all rumpled as soon as I left the room. Says he finds it hard to be still."

"That I can believe," smiled Janet.

"He's really a sweet little boy, though," said Tommie thoughtfully. "He reminds me of my little brother."

"You get personally interested in your patients, don't you, Tommie?" Janet asked curiously.

"Well, yes, I suppose I do," Tommie replied. "I've never been around sick people before, but I enjoy doing all I can to make them comfortable."

"You'll make a fine nurse someday, Tommie," Janet observed.

"Me? A nurse?" Tommie asked in surprise. "Oh, no, I'm not going to be a nurse! I'm going to be an artist."

Janet's dimples flashed in a smile. "Hm-m-m! We'll see! As I look into the future," she went on teasingly, "I see Tommie in the white uniform of a graduate nurse, with a black stripe on her cap and an R.N. after her name."

"No, you don't," Tommie interrupted, laughing. "I'm convinced you can't see into the future at all, or else it's someone else you see in that nurse's uniform. If you could see into the future, you'd see me in an artist's studio, not in a hospital!" She went on more seriously, "You see, Janet, ever since I can remember, Daddy has told me he would never permit one of his girls to be a nurse, even if she wanted to be one. During World War I he made rounds with his sister, a public-health nurse, and he's never forgotten. He says it's no life for a girl."

"Have you seen anything so bad about nursing here?" asked Janet.

"No," admitted Tommie.

"Probably nursing and nurses have changed since World War I," said Janet. "Anyway, I predict that before this summer is over you'll decide to become a nurse!"

By this time the girls had reached the dormitory, where Janet had a room. "I can't stay long, Janet," Tommie warned. "It's only a couple of hours until sunset, and I want to be ready for Sabbath before Aunt Marty and Delores get home. Oh, Janet, you just can't realize how I look forward to Sabbath, to MV meeting and Sabbath School, and everything!"

"Speaking of MV meeting tonight, have you heard we're going to have a real missionary for the speaker?" asked Janet eagerly.

"Are we really? Oh, that will be wonderful! I've read lots of mission stories, but I've never heard a missionary speak!" exclaimed Tommie.

The girls went into the dormitory. On entering the parlor, they found Anne and Phyllis already there.

"Oh, Tommie," Anne said eagerly, "would you do a favor for me?"

"I will if I can," Tommie answered.

"Well, you see," explained Anne, "Sandra and I are supposed to sing a duet at MV meeting tonight, but for some reason she hasn't come to practice yet. Would you practice with me? I'm not sure of the alto part, so if you'd sing the soprano, that would give me a chance to work on the harmony."

The song was one Tommie knew, so while Phyllis played, the two girls sang. Over and over they sang the song until finally Anne said, "Well, I think that will do. Thank you so much Tommie. That was a great help!"

After a short visit with Janet, Tommie walked the two blocks home from the dormitory, enjoying the lovely evening and chuckling to herself at Janet's idea of her as a nurse.

Tommie had finished her bath when Aunt Marty, Aunt Nola, and Delores came home. They were eager to hear about Tommie's day. As she explained about her patients and what she had done for them, Aunt Marty and Delores smiled at each other.

"Our Tommie is going to be a fine nurse one of these days," said Aunt Marty approvingly.

"Oh, no!" protested Tommie. "I'm going to be an artist." "Really," she thought, "this is just too much. Everyone is trying to make a nurse out of me, but I know what I want to be—an artist!"

"I think it would be a fine thing—" began Aunt Marty, but she was interrupted by a knock at the door. Anne stood just outside the screen. "Oh, come on in, Anne!"

"I came to see if Tommie would help me again," Anne explained a trifle breathlessly. "Sandra sent word that she has to stay with a patient who just had emergency surgery, so she can't sing with me tonight. I hurried over to see if Tommie would take Sandra's place. Will you, Tommie?"

"Oh, I couldn't possibly," gasped Tommie in dismay. "I can't sing well enough."

"But, Tommie," pleaded Anne, "we sang so well together this afternoon. Please don't refuse. There isn't time to work up another special number."

"I've never sung in public in all my life," said Tommie. "I'd be scared to death."

"No, you wouldn't! Why, I do it all the time!" said Anne. She was so anxious and pleading that Tommie finally let herself be persuaded to sing in Sandra's place. "Now, don't worry, everything will be all right," Anne reassured her as she left. "You sit with me up near the front, and I'll lead the way onto the platform when it is time for us to sing."

After Anne had gone, Delores said with a smile, "Lucky you! You'll get to sing for the visiting missionary!"

"That's quite an honor, Tommie," added Aunt Nola. "This is a special program, you know."

"Why," thought Tommie, "maybe it won't be so bad. In fact, it is rather nice to be considered good enough to sing for a special program." The more she thought about it the prouder she became. Before long she had convinced herself that it probably was a good thing that Sandra had been detained at the hospital—she'd probably do a better job than Sandra could have, anyway.

Tommie's courage did not desert her until she was sitting with Anne near the front of the church, waiting for the program to begin. Suddenly she shivered. Suppose she made a mistake and everyone laughed! She realized that her mouth was dry and her palms were wet. As well as she could remember, it should have been the other way around! What if she got up to sing and when she opened her

23

mouth not a sound emerged! Numbly she sat through the opening exercises.

Finally the duet was announced. Despairingly Tommie followed Anne to the platform. By now she was certain that not a note would come out when she opened her mouth to sing. But at least she'd have to try. The prelude was over. To Tommie's surprise her voice rang out clear and sure on the opening notes. She began to relax and sing with more confidence. "Why was I so scared?" she thought. "There's nothing to this at all!"

She and Anne stood with the book in their hands while Phyllis played a short interlude between the second and last verses of the song. Tommie heard a soft titter of amusement ripple through the audience. Glancing about, she saw a half-grown cat at the bottom of the platform steps. It marched deliberately up the steps and sat down directly in front of the two girls.

"Meow!" came it's questioning voice. "Meow!"

Tommie and Anne bravely began the last verse of the song in the face of the audience's growing amusement. But when the purring cat brushed against Tommie's legs, the girls' voices trailed off uncertainly as they joined the spectators' laughter.

Phyllis, her back to the singers, had not known what was going on. She looked around, hesitated, and played through the interlude again as one of the older boys picked up the cat and took it outside.

Tommie and Anne again started the final stanza of the song, but before they were through the first line, the cat came prancing in again through the open church door. He eluded the hands outstretched to stop him, and again brushed against Tommie's legs, purring and meowing as if he'd found a long-lost friend.

The audience's laughter grew in volume, and once more the girls' voices faltered and stopped. The cat was again taken outside, and Tommie and Anne tried heroically to finish their song. Breathless, embarrassed, their voices shaky, they sang. But giggles and laughter kept breaking out here and there all over the audience. At the end of the song Anne nudged Tommie, hissed, "Come on!" and walked abruptly from the platform.

Somehow the meeting went on, but everyone involved was unnerved and upset. One of the ushers dropped the offering plate and had to scramble for the money rolling down the aisles, and when the chorister announced a song, the pianist misunderstood the number and played something entirely different.

24

It was a little better when the missionary got up to speak. His stories kept the people's interest—all but Tommie's. Her mind wandered. She sat flushed and miserable, feeling as if the whole thing were her fault. She kept remembering how proud she'd felt, how she had thought she could probably do better than Sandra. "Sandra wouldn't have let herself be upset by that cat," Tommie thought. "Sandra—why, Sandra would have probably picked up the cat and held it in her arms while she finished the song, and instead of laughing, everyone would have felt respectful and admired her for her poise."

The meeting was finally over, and Tommie was glad to escape outside into the soft summer darkness to walk home with Aunt Marty and Delores. Her aunt and cousin tactfully did not refer to the meeting just past, and by the time they reached home Tommie had somewhat regained her composure, even to the point of conceding that it probably had been funny from an onlooker's viewpoint.

Many times during the next week, at meals, on duty, or coming to and from work, one or another of her friends would look at Tommie with a giggle and say softly, "Meow!" Tommie recognized that the laughter was not of ridicule, but only teasing, and she laughed along with the others.

Alone, however, she thought more seriously of the event. "Humility, that's what I'm learning," she said to herself; "and as usual, I'm learning it the hard way. If I'm ever again tempted to be proud of myself, I hope there will be someone nearby to whisper 'Meow.' That will bring me down in a hurry. I doubt that I'll ever forget this occasion when pride went before a fall!"

Questions | 5

"I'm going home this weekend, Tommie," Janet remarked as they sat at lunch. "I wish you could go along." Since Janet's home was only forty miles away, she could go there frequently.

"So do I," sighed Tommie. "But this is my Sabbath on duty. We've been lucky to get to work together most of the time, so I guess I shouldn't complain because our Sabbaths off duty don't coincide."

"I don't know how much longer we're going to work together," said Janet soberly. "I go on night duty when I get back!"

"Night duty!" exclaimed Tommie. "I'll miss you. I don't know what I'll do without you! Do you think you'll like night duty?"

"I don't know. The girls on night duty now say it isn't so bad. But I'll miss working with you."

"We've worked almost side by side all summer. It will seem strange not to be on the same shift you are on."

"I guess we'll just have to make the most of the time we have now. You can walk to the bus with me when I get ready to go home this afternoon—and carry my suitcase," Janet added impishly.

"You'd ask that of me?" Tommie demanded in mock horror. "After I've slaved on the wards all day, you'd ask me to carry your heavy old suitcase two whole blocks to the bus stop?"

"I guess we could put a stick through the handle and each carry one end," laughed Janet. "That wouldn't hurt either of us, since it's only a little overnight case and weighs little more than a patient's dinner tray."

"In that case you can count on me for assistance," Tommie announced, "but right now we'd better hurry back and make those two beds in the ward."

When work was finished for the afternoon, the two girls hurried down the road and stood waiting at the bus stop.

"You seem awfully happy to be going home this weekend, Janet," observed Tommie. "Any special reason?"

Janet flushed slightly, then laughed. "Well, yes— My boyfriend is going to be home too!"

"You mean that wonderful redheaded Johnny Hazen I've been hearing about all summer?" asked Tommie teasingly.

"Yes," admitted Janet. "But how did you know he is wonderful and redheaded?"

"You told me," giggled Tommie. "Let me count all the things you have told me about him. Let's see— We've already mentioned that he's redheaded. He's over six feet tall; the two of you have always gone to the same church, church school, and academy; he's working away from home this summer; his mother is an Adventist but his father is not; and Johnny plans to become a dentist. Right?"

"Right," laughed Janet. "Only I didn't realize that I'd talked so much about him. We're not engaged or anything. We are sort of going steady, I guess. Do you have a boyfriend, Tommie?"

"No," replied Tommie promptly. "I mean, nobody special. I like most of the boys at school, and some I like better than others. But I'm almost two years younger than you, Janet, and Mamma thinks I'm not old enough yet to become attached to any certain boy."

"There probably aren't any Adventist boys at your school, are there, Tommie?" asked Janet.

"No," Tommie answered. "Why do you ask?"

"Well, since Adventists aren't supposed to marry non-Adventists, it isn't a good idea to get interested in anyone who isn't a church member," replied Janet.

"I didn't know that," Tommie said thoughtfully, "but I can see why it would be so."

"In the academy we are always being warned against forming close friendships with boys outside the church," Janet went on.

"I'd love to attend an Adventist academy." Tommie said wistfully. "Last year Delores used to write and tell me how she enjoyed it."

"You'd love academy," Janet said. "We have the best times. I— Oh, oh! Here's my bus. I'll see you Monday, Tommie. Bye till then."

As Tommie walked back to Aunt Marty's house, she was deep in thought. Nearly every day she was learning something new about Adventists. It had never occurred to her that marriages between Adventists and non-Adventists were not approved, but as she thought about it, she realized how unwise such marriages would be. After all, her stand for the truth had caused all sorts of trouble at home, and she could see how such a difference in religious beliefs could make a marriage unhappy.

"Oh, well," she said to herself, "I'm too young to think of getting married. Still, when I do get married, it will be to an Adventist. I've had enough of standing alone in my beliefs. I'm not going to spend all my life defying a husband as I've had to defy Daddy about keeping the Sabbath."

All the next week Tommie missed Janet as she went about her work. They made a point of trying to have supper together every evening, and Janet told Tommie about night duty—how hard it was to keep awake sometimes, and how patient care differed at night. And Tommie told Janet how things were going during the day.

One Sabbath afternoon when Tommie returned from a walk, Aunt Marty said to her, "Tommie, Elder Keyes is having an effort in Norrisville, and a group of young people from here are going to attend tonight. Would you like to go along?"

"I'd love to," replied Tommie. "I want to make the most of every opportunity to learn about the church. Most of the girls here were born into Adventist homes, and I have a lot of catching up to do."

"You've learned a lot in a short time," commended Aunt Marty. "We've felt that your contact with Janet has been a big help to you. She is such a sincere Christian girl."

"I agree," said Tommie. "I've learned much from Janet. I miss her, though, since she's been on night duty."

"Miss Croft, the head nurse, mentioned to me today that she'd probably assign you to night duty, too, starting Monday night," Aunt Marty said.

"She did? I'm so glad. I think I'll like it," exclaimed Tommie. "Especially since I'll be on the same shift with Janet."

"We'd better go to supper now," said Aunt Marty with a glance at her watch. "You'll have to leave for Norrisville soon afterward."

That night the little church in Norrisville was nearly filled when the group from the hospital filed in and took their seats. After the song service Tommie sat alertly, for she knew that the messages of the church were given in full at these meetings, and she hoped that she'd learn something new.

Then her mind wandered back to the evening she had gone to church with Granny and Grandpa, when the minister had preached on the Ten Commandments.

"This is certainly different," she reflected. "Elder Keyes doesn't have to rely on tricks like ventriloquism to hold the people's attention. He just preaches the Bible. I've been fortunate to be a member of his congregation this summer."

The sermon began with a review of the signs of the end of the world. Tommie had heard of some of them—the dark day, the falling of the stars, the great earthquake, and others. Then Elder Keyes began to develop his main theme—something else that was to come before the end—a time of great trouble.

Tommie listened intently, and as the minutes wore on, she became more and more frightened. There was to be a time of trouble such as never was before—the members of the remnant church would be pursued, imprisoned, some even meeting death. It was horrible! A smothering curtain of terror dropped over Tommie's mind, and she didn't hear the last part of the sermon.

Her thoughts were racing. "I'm afraid. I know I won't be able to stand true in times like that! I'm a coward! I'm afraid of being hurt. What shall I do? Oh, I wish I'd never come here tonight. But maybe it's better to know about these things ahead of time. Why is God going to let something like that happen? I've had enough trouble. I don't want any more! Maybe being an Adventist isn't worth it."

The meeting was over, and Tommie, still greatly troubled by what she had heard, sat quietly as the car sped back to the hospital. She wished she were better acquainted with the other young people in the car, but they were all student nurses, and she felt she didn't know any of them well enough to talk about what was bothering her. How she wished she could talk to Janet. What did Adventist young people think about this time of trouble, anyhow? Weren't they afraid? Did they have some inner strength she didn't possess?

She tossed restlessly that night and arose still tired and frightened the next morning. Her usual optimism about the future had been dampened. She had found that usually the things you dread are never as bad as you expect them to be. But Elder Keyes had made it clear that people couldn't imagine how bad that time of trouble was to be.

To Tommie, in her uneasy state of mind, the day seemed endless. Finally it was suppertime. When she arrived at the cafeteria, she found that Janet had just left, having eaten earlier than usual because her brother had come for a visit. Tommie went home without bothering to eat.

She paced the floor restlessly, back and forth. At last she said aloud. "All right! I might as well face it. There is only one way out. I won't become a Seventh-day Adventist." After she had made her decision she threw herself on her bed and cried as if her heart would break.

At noon the next day the head nurse called Tommie into her office and told her to go off duty at one o'clock and then come back on night duty at midnight. It was the only bright spot in the past two days of Tommie's life. At least she and Janet would be working together again.

As Tommie walked listlessly home at one o'clock, she thought of Daddy. He, too, had decided against the Adventist Church, and Tommie felt sure he hadn't been really happy since.

"I probably won't be happy, either," she reflected, "but I'm too much of a coward to face what's ahead!"

She'd forgotten it was Aunt Marty's afternoon off. As soon as she entered the house her aunt looked up and said firmly, "Tommie, something is troubling you! I've noticed it for two days now. Aren't you happy here? Are you homesick?"

"No, I'm not homesick," replied Tommie. "It's just that—well, I—I've decided not to become an Adventist!"

"And the decision has left you unhappy?" queried Aunt Marty.

"Yes," admitted Tommie. "I was unhappy before I made it, and I wasn't any happier after I made it. I thought I would be, but I'm not!"

"Do you want to tell me about it?" asked Aunt Marty.

Tommie found it a great relief to pour out the whole story, ending with, "Since I am so afraid, I felt the only way to escape all that trouble was not to be an Adventist."

Her aunt nodded gravely. "I see," she murmured. "Tommie, when your daddy threatened to beat you for keeping the Sabbath, weren't you afraid?"

"Yes, I was," said Tommie. "I was scared half to death. But that was different," she went on earnestly. "I knew exactly what I was afraid of. I knew my punishment would be painful, but I wasn't in danger of being killed. Anyhow, it seemed different to me."

"How did you meet your fear then, Tommie?" Aunt Marty went on.

"I prayed, and the Lord helped me," Tommie said. "But, Aunt Marty, this trouble that is ahead is so awful—"

"Do you doubt that God is able to help you in the time of trouble ahead? Don't you feel that He can help you just as He did before?"

Tommie sat silently a few moments, thinking. "My problem has been a lack of faith, hasn't it?" she said finally.

"Tommie, surely Elder Keyes mentioned in his sermon that God would help us through that time of trouble. Didn't he?" asked Aunt Marty.

"Maybe he did," Tommie admitted slowly, "only I was so scared and upset I didn't hear the last part of his sermon."

"When a person gets discouraged or frightened, Satan can take advantage of the circumstances and lead him astray. Just remember, Tommie, the Lord will see us through all the way to the kingdom. Sister White says that in one of her visions she was with the redeemed in heaven and that their testimony was that heaven was more than worth the trouble they had gone through."

Tommie took a deep breath, as though a heavy weight had been lifted. Her troubled mind was at rest.

"Tommie," observed Aunt Marty, "do you realize this is the first time in two days you've smiled?"

"I didn't feel like smiling," Tommie said. "But I do now. I feel wonderful."

"I'm glad you do," Aunt Marty smiled. "Now, I think you'd better go to bed and get some sleep. The first night on night duty can be hard. It will be a few days before you adjust to sleeping in the day and working at night."

"I haven't slept well the past two nights," Tommie confessed, "but now that I am not troubled anymore, I think I can sleep. Thank you, Aunt Marty, for helping me through this."

"Tommie, there are certain to be other things you don't understand as you learn more truth. Don't be afraid to ask questions. Your Aunt Nola and I will be glad to help you. Don't try to carry all these problems by yourself. We are praying for you, and we want to see you a faithful member of the remnant church."

"I'll remember, Aunt Marty," promised Tommie. "I'll be a star in your crown someday, I hope."

"I hope so too," said Aunt Marty. "Now, run along to bed and sleep!"

"My, it's good to have my world right side up again," Tommie thought as she nestled drowsily between the sheets. "From now on I'll not try to bear my burdens by myself, and I'll always remember that with God's help I can face anything—even the time of trouble!"

Night Duty | 6

Tommie hadn't told Janet that she was going on night duty, and she smiled as she thought how surprised Janet would be.

As she entered the door of the hospital she noticed that the clock in the hall said one minute past midnight. Tommie was to be on duty on second floor, so she hurried to the stairs and ran up.

A fierce "S-h-h-h-h! !" brought her to a sudden halt. On the landing above her stood Mrs. Sorensen, the night supervisor. She shook her finger at Tommie as she admonished in a stern whisper, "Miss Gordon, don't you ever, ever, run up the steps at night! The sounds at night are magnified, and you'll wake every patient on the floor! Please remember!"

"I'll remember," Tommie promised meekly, and came up the rest of the stairs on tiptoe. She thought to herself, "This is certainly a fine beginning—getting the supervisor angry before I even get on the floor."

"Come on, Miss Gordon," the supervisor continued in a more lenient whisper, "and I'll tell you a little about night duty. You'll have the patients' call lights to answer just as you do on day shift. There will be temperatures to take and sometimes treatments to give. In general you just help the nurses. You realize that you'll have to be quieter, and you'll have to take a flashlight with you when you go around looking after the patients. Sometime during the night, unless we are exceptionally busy, you will have two hours off to sleep. A lunch is served at midnight. Right now I want you to go up to room 302 and stay with Miss Shafer's patient while she has lunch."

Tommie went up to third floor, which was cared for by the second-floor nurses. She remembered to go quietly. The door to room 302 was open, and Tommie could see Janet sitting there, writing.

"S-s-s-t, Janet!"

"Tommie!" Janet exclaimed in surprise. "What are you doing up here this time of night?"

"I couldn't sleep," answered Tommie, "so I thought I'd just come up and visit with you awhile."

"You're in uniform," Janet pointed out suspiciously.

"Oh, that," Tommie explained airily. "Well, I didn't want to turn on all the lights at home and wake up everyone, so I just put on the first clothes my hands touched. Lucky it was my uniform, though— now maybe nobody will notice I'm here when I'm not supposed to be. They'll think I'm on duty!"

Janet looked uncertain, wavering between whether to laugh at Tommie's prank or to be alarmed for fear Tommie would get caught and punished.

Suddenly Tommie grinned. "Run along, Miss Shafer. I'm the new night nurse's aide, come to relieve you for lunch!"

Janet's grin matched Tommie's. "You rascal," she laughed. "I'm so glad you're on nights too!"

"What is to be done for your patient while you're gone?" Tommie asked.

"Nothing," replied Janet. "He has pneumonia, and he's in a coma. I've given him fomentations, and he's not due to have more until four o'clock. I'll be back before it's time to take his temperature again."

Janet slipped quietly away, and Tommie sat in the chair Janet had vacated. She picked up the patient's chart and read it to see what Janet had been required to do for him. Beyond giving fomentations and taking his temperature periodically there was little for Janet to do, she noted.

As she read the chart a slip of paper fell out and fluttered to the floor. Tommie picked it up, and thinking it was something about the patient, she scanned it. There in Janet's neat handwriting were written over and over the words, "Mrs. Johnny Hazen," "Mrs. John A. Hazen," "Mrs. J. A. Hazen," "Janet and Johnny Hazen," "Janet Hazen." Tommie smiled and slipped the paper back into the chart.

When Janet returned, Tommie arose and handed her the chart. Again the little piece of paper slipped out and fluttered to the floor. Tommie stopped, retrieved it and slowly handed it back to Janet, who bulshed a fiery red.

"Did you have a nice weekend when you were home, Janet?" asked Tommie with a smile.

"Yes— Yes, I did," Janet stammered. Suddenly both girls began to giggle helplessly and Janet held out the slip of paper to Tommie, saying, "Look at it if you want to—after all, a girl is entitled to her dreams!"

"Your dreams may be near to coming true," observed Tommie.

"Yes, they are," admitted Janet. "Johnny and I had some serious talks about the future. We each have another year in the academy, and then he wants to go to college. If we still feel the same after he has finished two years of college, we'll be married. We're not engaged, really—we're engaged to be engaged, if you know what I mean."

"I don't, but that's all right," said Tommie.

"I mean, with the war and all, we can't plan too definitely," said Janet. "Besides, we're young yet, and lots of things may change in the next three years. One couple in our class is engaged, and they plan to be married as soon as school is out next year. I think they are too young, but I guess they don't feel that way. Anyway, it's fun to make plans, even if nothing ever comes of them."

"I guess it is," agreed Tommie. "I'll probably never have any plans of that kind. I don't know where I'll meet any Adventist boys."

"You will someday," Janet assured her. "Adventists always meet other Adventists."

"I'd better go back downstairs and get to work. I've already gotten one black mark in Mrs. Sorensen's book tonight, and I don't want to get any more—I'll tell you about it later," said Tommie as she turned to leave.

The night wore on. Tommie slept from 2 to 4 a.m. and then sat with Janet's patient while Janet slept until 6. After that there were all sorts of things to do as the nurses and aides came on duty to get the patients ready for breakfast. Tommie helped take temperatures, cleaned the nursery, straightened up the wards, and washed the equipment that had been used during the night.

Finally it was time to go off duty. "Well, that wasn't so bad," Tommie remarked to Janet as they descended the stairs to breakfast.

"The first night on night duty usually isn't," Janet replied.

Tommie looked at her in astonishment. "But everyone says—" she began.

"I know, I know," said Janet. "But from my own experience, I'll tell you that it's the second night on night duty that's really bad. It is just agony to try to stay awake, and when a patient puts on her call light and says, 'Nurse, I can't sleep,' you'll have to bite your tongue to keep from saying, 'Well, just change places with me for an hour—you work in my place and I'll sleep in yours.'"

Tommie had to laugh at Janet's rueful picture but admitted it probably wasn't far from the truth.

The next night proved the veracity of Janet's prediction. Tommie *did* find it hard to keep awake. A registered nurse took care of the man Janet had sat with the night before, so Janet was doing floor duty along with Tommie. It would have been easier to keep awake if the work had been harder, but lights to answer were few and far between.

Janet was well adjusted to night duty by now and was inclined to laugh at Tommie's efforts to keep her eyes open.

"All right, laugh if you want to," said Tommie, a trifle irritated. "It's really no laughing matter, though."

"I'm sorry, Tommie," smiled Janet. "I know it isn't a laughing matter. Will you forgive me if I promise to show you something that's guaranteed to keep you awake?"

"Of course I'll forgive you," answered Tommie, "but I don't believe there's anything that will keep me awake much longer."

"Wait here and see," said Janet as she walked away.

Tommie stood by the desk, thinking how wonderful it would be to sleep for only five minutes. In fact, it would be wonderful to be able to just close her eyes—

Something cold and wet slid down her back inside her uniform. She straightened up with a gasp, clapping her hand over her mouth to keep from exclaiming aloud, and turning to see Janet's dimples twinkling at her.

"Now are you awake?" laughed Janet.

"Yes, I am," shivered Tommie. "Is that ice?"

"Yes, that's ice," admitted Janet. "We all resort to ice cubes down our backs now and then when the going gets rough. See," turning her back so Tommie could see the damp streak down it. "I used some myself so you wouldn't feel mistreated and picked on!"

That night also passed, and within a week Tommie was finding it much easier to stay awake.

One night when she came on duty Mrs. Sorensen met her and said, "Miss Gordon, you are to sit with a patient in the sanitarium building tonight. Report to Miss Melville on first floor, and she will take you over and tell you what you're to do."

As Miss Melville and Tommie went along the covered walkway between the hospital and sanitarium buildings, Miss Melville explained, "This patient has had a nervous breakdown. She isn't very ill, but her family wants someone with her at night. She's had a heavy sedative, so you will be allowed to doze now and then—just don't go sound asleep for any length of time."

As they entered the sanitarium, Miss Melville showed Tommie a button on the wall. "If you should need me, just push that button and I'll come right away," she said. "It turns on a light at the first floor nurses' station."

Tommie stood inside the doorway of the room and studied her patient, a middle-aged woman who was sound asleep. A towel had been pinned about the shade of the floor lamp so there would be some light in the room but not enough to disturb the patient.

Tommie sank down gratefully into the comfortable, upholstered chair. It was too early to be sleepy but it was nice to rest for a bit and let her thoughts wander.

She and Janet had gone to town that afternoon, and Tommie had taken a part of her monthly pay and bought herself a watch. It wasn't a wristwatch—it was a watch that pinned into the pocket of her uniform and could be pulled out on a chain which would wind back by spring action when the watch was released. It was white, made especially for nurses, and Tommie was immensely proud of it. Now she wouldn't have to borrow a watch when she had to take temperatures.

She pulled the watch out and looked at it. Maybe when she went home she and her friend Lucinda could trade watches part of the time. Lucinda had always been generous about letting Tommie wear her wristwatch. Thinking of Lucinda brought to Tommie's mind the fact that she hadn't answered the letter she had received from Lucinda that week. Now would be a good time to write, Tommie decided.

The letter, written on the note pad Tommie carried in her pocket, took some time to finish. Then she went to lunch while Janet watched her patient. Afterward she dozed at intervals.

Tommie was awake when her patient stirred.

"Nurse?" came the tentative voice.

"Yes, Mrs. Fenton?" said Tommie, coming to the bedside.

The patient peered up at her. "Are you the nurse?"

"Yes, I am for tonight," Tommie answered.

"Oh!" Mrs. Fenton was silent for a few moments, then spoke again. "Nurse, I want an orange."

"Oh, I'm sorry, Mrs. Fenton, but the oranges are in the kitchen over in the other building," explained Tommie. "Why don't you go back to sleep, and I'll leave a note saying you want an orange at breakfast?"

"But I don't want to sleep. I've already been asleep. And I don't want an orange at breakfast—I want one right now," Mrs. Fenton muttered petulantly.

"But Mrs. Fenton—" began Tommie.

"Wait a minute," commanded the patient, sitting up and fumbling with her purse which had been placed on the bedside table. Tommie watched wonderingly, puzzled at an odd note in the patient's voice.

"Ah, here it is," exclaimed Mrs. Fenton triumphantly, holding up a large pocket knife and extending the blade. "Now, see here, nurse, this is a knife, and we wouldn't want anyone to get hurt with it, would we?" she went on craftily. "I wouldn't want to have to hurt you, but—" She let the sentence hang, suggestively.

Tommie shivered, and for some reason she remembered the night Janet had used the ice to keep her awake—the sensation down her back was the same as it had been then.

"Oh, please, Lord, tell me what to do," she prayed.

"Are you going to get me that orange, nurse?"

"We don't have any oranges here, Mrs. Fenton," Tommie tried to explain, very much aware that her voice was none too steady. "I'm not allowed to go over to the other building now, either. I—"

The patient interrupted. "My husband brought me a sack of oranges this afternoon, and the nurse put them in that refrigerator where the medicines are kept, right there in that room across the hall. I want one of those oranges right now!"

Tommie arose and was surprised to find that her trembling legs supported her. In the refrigerator across the hall she found the sack of oranges marked with her patient's name. She pushed the button that would summon the first floor nurse, and breathing a prayer for help she reentered the room.

"I see you found the oranges," Mrs. Fenton said approvingly. "Peel one for me!"

"I don't—I don't have a knife," replied Tommie. "May I—borrow yours?"

"Yes, of course." Mrs. Fenton handed the knife to Tommie.

Tommie bent her head over the task of peeling the orange and sent a prayer of thanks heavenward. She handed the orange to Mrs. Fenton just as Miss Melville appeared at the door.

37

In the hall Tommie explained the situation and gave the knife to Miss Melville.

"It was clever of you to get the knife from her that way," commended Miss Melville.

"I prayed," said Tommie, "and the Lord helped me know what to do."

"I'll go over and get another sedative for Mrs. Fenton," said Miss Melville. "I don't think you'll have any more trouble with her tonight."

Twenty minutes later Mrs. Fenton was sleeping soundly, but Tommie didn't doze the rest of the night.

Shortly before time for Tommie to go off duty her patient stirred, yawned, and sat up. "Hello," she smiled at Tommie. "I haven't seen you before, have I?"

"Last night was the first night I ever took care of you," Tommie hedged.

"I really slept last night," remarked Mrs. Fenton cheerfully. "I never woke up once!"

"That's fine," answered Tommie. "I hope you have a nice day!"

"Thank you, dear," came the response.

Tommie stopped at the sanitarium nurses' desk to report. After telling her story, she added, "She doesn't seem to remember one thing about what happened. She says she never awakened at all last night."

"I'm not surprised," answered the charge nurse. "Things often happen that way."

At the sanitarium door Tommie met Janet.

"Come on, Tommie," she said. "I'm as hungry as a bear. We really worked hard over on second floor last night, while you, you lucky thing, had a soft job of special duty. Tell me, what kind of night did you have anyway? Get any sleep?"

"Oh, Janet," exclaimed Tommie. "Just wait till I tell you!"

Tommie took a final look in the mirror. Her gray uniform was clean and starched, her shoes newly polished, her hair smooth and neat beneath the hairnet. She was ready to go to work—almost.

Taking her new Bible from her bedside table, she read the Morning Watch text. Both Bible and Morning Watch Calendar were gifts from Aunt Nola. The first evening after Tommie had arrived in Brownsburg the family had prepared for evening worship. Tommie brought out her Bible—the remains she had found in the box of books that had belonged to her grandma. Aunt Nola had asked, "Is that the only Bible you have, Tommie!"

"Yes," replied Tommie. "It used to be Grandma's. Daddy brought home a box of her books, and this was in it."

Aunt Nola took the Book and held it gently in her hands. "Mother read this until it literally fell apart," she said with a catch in her voice.

Nothing more was said about it at the time, but several days later Aunt Nola presented a new Bible to Tommie. It was a lovely Bible with a leather cover, on which "TOMMIE GORDON" was stamped in gold letters. Tommie loved it and used it, but the old one that had belonged to Grandma was safely packed away in Tommie's suitcase. It was still very dear to her.

Tommie finished the Morning Watch text, knelt for prayer, and then hurried to the girls' dormitory to meet Janet. Together they walked up the hill. Morning worship in the chapel came after breakfast, and then it was time to go on duty.

Tommie had only three baths on her list that morning. That was not a heavy assignment, and there were not as many patients as usual on her floor. Tommie liked it that way, for it meant that she could spend more time with each patient. It also meant that sometime during the day she might be sent to help out on another floor where there were more patients.

Tommie had just finished the last bath on her list when she was stopped by one of the student nurses. "Miss Gordon," she said, "we have a little boy in Room 304 who had surgery yesterday. His parents have gone to get some rest and he's crying for them. It is very important that he be kept quiet. Do you think you can amuse him for an hour?"

"I'll try," said Tommie. "How old is he?"

"He's five," replied the student.

"I'll go right up there," Tommie promised.

"Fine! His parents said they'd be back at 11:30, so it really won't be too long."

As Tommie entered the room, she heard the small boy sobbing over and over, "I want my mommy! I want my daddy!"

"May I stay here with you for a while?" asked Tommie.

"Yes, only I want my mommy," he sobbed.

"She will be back soon," soothed Tommie. "She needed some rest. I'll stay with you until she comes. Now let's get acquainted. What's your name?"

"Tommy," he said.

"It is?" said Tommie. "Why, that's my name too!"

He looked at her incredulously, forgetting to cry. "But you're a *girl!*"

"I know," said Tommie. "That's what everyone says when I tell them my name. Tell me, do you like pictures?"

"Yes," came the answer.

Tommie took her pencil and note pad from her pocket and began drawing animal pictures for him. His questions led her into telling stories about them, and it seemed only a few minutes until his parents came in.

"This is my very own nurse," the little boy said proudly to his mother. "When you want to go rest some more she'll come back and play with me—won't you?" he appealed to Tommie.

"Of course," promised Tommie. "I'll come and see you every day until you are well enough to go home."

Reporting back to the nurses' station, Tommie was sent to lunch so she could be back in time to deliver the patients' trays. Janet was sent at the same time. The charge nurses, knowing of the friendship between the two girls, usually assigned them together, both as to hours on duty and work assignments.

In the middle of the afternoon Tommie gathered the patients' water pitchers onto a cart and took them to the utility room. There she scrubbed each pitcher and tray, replacing name and room tags as needed. She filled the pitchers with ice water, and, after placing a clean glass on each tray, took the fresh water back to the patients.

This was a job most of the aides disliked, but Tommie loved it. One day Janet questioned her about it. "I don't see why you like it so much, Tommie," Janet said. "It seems that whenever I take the water pitchers around, every patient wants something else done—a pillow fluffed, or a sheet straightened, or a surgical binder tightened, or something. Don't they ask you to do those things, too?"

"Yes, they do," Tommie answered with a twinkle in her eye, "but I tell them just to be patient for a few more minutes and I'll send Miss Janet Shafer in to take care of the things they want done!"

"Oh, come on, Tommie," persisted Janet, laughing in spite of herself, "tell me why you like to fill the water pitchers!"

"All right, Janet," replied Tommie, suddenly serious. "Here's why. Jesus says that a cup of cold water given in His name is as if we were giving it to Him. I like to think of all the cups of cold water I give to Him by filling the patients' water pitchers every afternoon. As for the little things the patients want done as I bring them their water, well, I rather enjoy doing them. That way I get acquainted with every patient on the floor rather than just the ones on my list."

Janet looked at Tommie with new respect in her eyes. "I see what you mean," she said thoughtfully. "I had never thought of the water pitchers in that way before."

"It isn't only the water pitchers, Janet," Tommie replied soberly. "Everything we do for our patients we should do as unto the Lord."

When Tommie finished giving out the water pitchers that afternoon, one of the graduates in charge came to the desk and said, "If you're through here, Miss Gordon, will you go down on first floor and help awhile? Miss Cox and the student are alone down there, and they could use the help of an aide."

"Yes, Miss Hansen. I'll go right away," said Tommie.

On first floor the student nurse asked Tommie to take the temperatures in the men's ward. The rest of the temperatures had already been taken. Tommie went into the ward and placed a thermometer in the mouth of the first patient. Then taking his wrist she began to count his pulse. After a few seconds she realized something was wrong. His pulse was strong and regular and it didn't seem to be too rapid, yet according to her watch—

He had been watching her with an amused expression. Then he spoke around the thermometer, "Something wrong, nurse?"

"Yes, there is," blurted Tommie. "Either my watch has stopped or you're dead!"

His whoop of laughter startled her. She made a wild grab and retrieved the thermometer before it slipped down his throat, while he lay there laughing with tears streaming down his face.

Miss Cox heard the noise and came in quickly. "What's the trouble here, Miss Gordon?" she asked in her most professional, starched-uniform voice.

Tommie, her face crimson, stammered, but could find nothing to say that would answer Miss Cox's question. The patient came to her rescue. Still wiping tears from his eyes, he said weakly, "She said something funny!"

"I've noticed she has a way of doing that," Miss Cox said drily, and walked out.

Fifteen minutes later Tommie, having wound her watch so that it was working again, finished the temperatures and took the list to the nurses' station. Miss Cox was just leaving as Tommie entered.

"Is she going to scold me for what happened in the ward a little while ago?" Tommie wondered as Miss Cox paused in front of her. Miss Cox placed a hand on Tommie's shoulder and said quietly, "A merry heart doeth good like a medicine!" smiled briefly, and went on about her work.

Tommie let out a breath she hadn't realized she was holding, shook her head and said to herself, "That's one thing about a hospital: It's full of surprises."

Soon it was time for supper trays. Tommie helped deliver them and then went to feed the little girl in Room 103. Connie was about two years old, and she was an active, noisy child.

As Tommie entered the room, Connie jumped up and down in the crib, shrieking, "Nursie, Connie hungry! Nursie, Connie yuv' you!"

Tommie tied the bib around Connie's neck and began to feed her. The child had a good appetite and ate each bite with relish. Now and then, between bites, she would throw her arms around Tommie and declare, "Nursie, Connie yuv' you."

When the meal was ended, Tommie untied the bib from around Connie's neck and washed the sticky little face and hands. She thought to herself. "Children are the nicest patients! When I get to be a nurse—" She stopped, startled at her own thoughts. Sometime, somehow, she had made the decision to be a nurse without even being consciously aware of it. Perhaps it had been growing all summer, each day adding something new to the pleasure she found in caring for the sick. At some point during the summer her ambition to be an artist had disappeared so quietly she hadn't been aware of its going, and this new dream had taken its place.

As Tommie stood there lost in these thoughts she became aware of a voice speaking to her. "You go by-by, nursie? Huh? You go by-by?"

"Oh—yes, Connie, I'm going by-by!"

"You come back, nursie?"

"Of course, Connie. I'll be back tomorrow! Be a good girl now."

"Connie always goo' girl," said the little girl as Tommie left. "By-by, nursie!"

Work was over for the day. As the two friends walked down the hill together, Janet asked, as she had so often before, "Well, Tommie, have you decided to become a nurse?"

"Yes, I have," replied Tommie.

Janet talked blithely on, for she had not really heard Tommie's answer. "You will yet, you wait and see! Before the summer is— *What was that you said, Tommie?*"

"I just said that I have decided to become a nurse," Tommie said quietly, but her eyes sparkled mischievously.

"I knew it! I knew it! I just knew you would! Didn't I tell you and tell you?" Janet was nearly beside herself with joy at seeing her predictions fulfilled.

"I believe you said something about it a few times," Tommie replied, laughing.

"I'm so glad, Tommie, because I've seen all along how you enjoy the work and how well you do it," Janet went on.

"That wasn't the reason at all, Janet," Tommie teased. "It's just that with your nagging at me to become a nurse I decided I'd have to if I ever wanted any peace!"

"Tommie," suggested Janet, "if you have decided to be a nurse, why don't you stay here until after graduation? You'd enjoy seeing the seniors get their diplomas after you've been working with them all summer."

"I'll have to write home and see if I can miss the first few days of school," said Tommie. "I really would like to see the graduation."

That night she wrote and asked Mamma if she could stay a few days longer, telling her how much she wanted to attend the graduation. She did not tell Mamma that she had decided to become a nurse, because she knew Daddy wouldn't like that at all. She would break that news to him at a later date. Mamma wrote back that she had asked the school principal if Tommie could miss the first few days of school, and he had said it would be all right.

The night of graduation came. Tommie sat with Janet, looking quietly around the little church and thinking back over the summer. It had been wonderful to go to church and Sabbath School, to learn more about Adventist beliefs. She knew she would never forget the friends she had made. Her bags were packed—she would be leaving for home early in the morning—but she'd come back. Maybe she'd come back the next summer.

The organ strains of "Pomp and Circumstance" announced that the graduation exercises had begun. Tommie watched intently, highly impressed with the inspiring graduation address and the simple ceremony that followed.

The seniors repeated the Nightingale Pledge:

"I solemnly pledge myself before God and in the presence of this assembly:

"To pass my life in purity and to practice my profession faithfully.

"I will abstain from whatever is deleterious and mischievous, and will not take or knowingly administer any harmful drug.

"I will do all in my power to maintain and elevate the standard of my profession, and will hold in confidence all personal matters committed to my keeping and all family affairs coming to my knowledge in the practice of my profession.

"With loyalty will I endeavor to aid the physician in his work and devote myself to the welfare of those committed to my care."

Then they marched across the platform to receive their diplomas that were the goal of three years' work.

Tommie said in her heart, "Someday I'll walk across that platform for my diploma!"

Senior Days | 8

"Hi, Lu, come back and sit by me," called Tommie as Lucinda boarded the school bus.

"Hi, Tommie," greeted Lucinda with as much warmth as if they hadn't seen each other in weeks, although in truth they had spent the previous afternoon visiting. The girls had remained staunch friends through the years, although Lucinda forbade Tommie to talk to her about her religion.

"Isn't it exciting, Lucinda? Just think! This year we are grand old seniors," exclaimed Tommie.

"It really is. And I'm going to make the most of it. After this year our class will be scattered all over," said Lucinda.

"I wonder if there will be anybody new in our class this year?" pondered Tommie. "That's one of the things that makes the first day of school so interesting—new teachers and new classmates."

"This will likely be the last school year together for most of us," said Lucinda thoughtfully. "Most of the boys will go into service right after graduation, and the girls will get jobs somewhere."

"Few of us can afford college," agreed Tommie. "I'm lucky to be going into nurses' training next year in a hospital where I can work my way through."

"I hear that Edward and Paul aren't coming back to school this year," said Lu.

"Too bad," replied Tommie. "Our class grows smaller and smaller. Remember there were thirty-one of us the year we were freshmen? And last year there were only fifteen."

When the senior class met in the room that had been designated their homeroom, the members were pleased to note that there was an addition to their number. He had dark, wavy hair, eyebrows that almost met above his nose, blue eyes, and a smile that was all the more interesting because it quirked slightly higher on one side.

Tommie noticed the flutter of interest among the girls as they tried to observe him without being too obvious. She sighed. It was not likely that this boy was an Adventist, not if that bulge in his shirt pocket indicated cigarettes.

It had been hard during her junior year, feeling so left out of school activities. Most of her friends were dating, but Tommie had refused all dates, and soon the boys stopped asking. They knew it was because of her religion, but they never really understood it. Larry had been a little more persistent than the others, trying to persuade her that since his grandmother was an Adventist and he understood all their beliefs, he was more acceptable as a date than the others.

Larry once said to her after she refused a date with him, "Why don't you come to the ball game with me? Who knows, maybe you could make an Adventist out of me."

For a moment Tommie was tempted. It would be fun to have a date and go to the ball game; and maybe Larry was right—maybe she could persuade him to become an Adventist. For a moment she wavered, then her resolve stiffened.

"No, Larry, I'm sorry. If your grandma hasn't been able to make an Adventist out of you after all these years, I wouldn't have a chance. After all, she knows more about the Adventist Church than I do!"

He had laughed and gone on his way, and Tommie had spent her evenings studying. At least, she got good grades.

Now here was her final year in high school, probably doomed to be as lonely as the last year had been.

At noon the senior girls met in the study hall to eat lunch together.

"Say, isn't that new boy cute?" exclaimed Viola. "Does anybody know his name?"

"I do," answered Reatha. "It's Jimmy Don Brewer. I met him this summer."

"Have you ever dated him?" asked Margaret.

"No," answered Reatha. "I'm going steady with Edward. In fact, we're engaged."

Most of the girls broke into delighted cries at this news, and Reatha blushingly revealed that she and Edward were going to be married as soon as school was out.

By the end of the week, school and classwork had settled into a fixed routine. Tommie had been elected vice-president of the senior class, and her classmates were already teasing her about what she should include in the valedictorian address at graduation.

One evening Tommie and her mother were discussing the class. Three of the class members had gone to school together since first grade, and most of the rest had joined the class during the freshman year.

"I've been hearing you mention this Jimmy Don," Mamma said. "What is his last name?"

"Brewer," answered Tommie.

"Jimmy Don Brewer!" exclaimed Mamma. "Why, of course! That is Alvin and Laurie Brewer's oldest boy. We lived next to them when you and Jimmy Don were little. You used to play together until they moved away."

As the days went by Tommie was aware that nearly every girl in the class, except Reatha and herself, was trying to get a date with Jimmy Don. So far he had dated none of them. He was pleasant, often teased, but never showed any partiality. Tommie knew he was the most handsome boy she'd ever seen. She realized that when he teased her, as he did the others, she stood speechless, unable to think of a single bright remark to make in response. She could tease any of the other boys right back, but not Jimmy Don. She felt a sense of uneasiness because of this, but in the closeness of school life she could not avoid him. She wasn't sure she even wanted to.

One day as the class stood outside the door of the typing room, Jimmy Don looked from his height of six feet down to Tommie's mere five feet three inches and loftily inquired, "And what do you want to be when you grow up?"

Tommie was painfully aware that any of the other girls would have had a clever quip to give in answer, but all she could do was stammer and finally say, "A nurse!"

He flashed the smile that always gave her a prickly feeling in the pit of her stomach and said, "Personally, I think you'd make a better doctor. From now on, like it or not, you're going to be 'Doc Gordon.'"

Tommie looked up, startled. She had told absolutely no one, not even Lucinda and Janet, about the ambitious dream she was harboring—that of going beyond nursing and becoming a doctor. Before she could say anything, the classroom door was opened and they trooped into typing class.

Several classmates commented curiously on the fact that Jimmy Don always called Tommie "Doc" after that, but Tommie couldn't explain why, and Jimmy Don didn't.

One day Tommie sat down and gave herself a stern talking-to. "I

47

just can't afford to go falling in love with Jimmy Don Brewer," she said to herself. "He isn't an Adventist, for one thing. He smokes. Besides, I have at least three more years of schooling after this one before I become a nurse, and I don't want anything to stand in the way of that." Then she laughed wryly at herself and continued. "I guess it is a bit presumptuous of me to get all up in the air over this. After all, he's never shown a preference for any girl in school, and certainly not for me. For all we know, he may have a steady girl friend somewhere else. And if he should happen to ask me for a date, I'd just have to say 'No, thank you' as I've always done before to the other boys." But in her heart she knew it would be much harder to refuse a date with Jimmy Don than it would with one of her other classmates.

The next morning Jimmy Don stopped Tommie in the hall and said, "Doc, my folks tell me that you and I were playmates when we were little kids."

"That's what Mamma told me, too," Tommie managed to answer.

"Well, how about renewing an old acquaintance? Will you go with me to the ball game Thursday night?"

Tommie forgot that she'd promised herself to say "No, thanks," if Jimmy Don ever asked her for a date. Instead she answered promptly, "I'd love to," and that was that.

Tommie and Jimmy Don's arrival together at the ball game on Thursday night caused a minor sensation. Tommie had to admit to herself that she enjoyed the attention they attracted.

Margaret and Viola caught her alone for a few minutes and demanded to know how Tommie had managed to get a date with Jimmy Don when none of the other girls had been able to. Viola hinted teasingly at blackmail, and Margaret said that maybe Jimmy Don had needed help with his schoolwork. Tommie could only laugh and fend off their questions—after all, she herself didn't know how it had happened.

Thereafter Tommie and Jimmy Don dated about once a week, usually going to ball games or class parties. The first—and only—time Jimmy Don ever asked Tommie to go to the movies with him, she explained why she couldn't go, wondering if he'd ever ask her for another date. He nodded thoughtfully as she talked.

"I wondered if your religion wasn't what made you different from the other girls. I haven't felt free to smoke when you're around, Doc. Larry told me that Adventists don't smoke. What else do they believe?"

That question opened the way for a whole series of talks on religion. Jimmy Don continued to ask Tommie for dates, and after ball games and parties they often spent an hour or more discussing the Bible. It was evident from his interest that Jimmy Don enjoyed these talks.

One afternoon as Lucinda and Tommie waited for the bus, Lu turned to Tommie and said, "You're having more fun this year than you did last year, aren't you, Tommie?"

Tommie thought over all the good times she hadn't had to miss this year and answered happily, "I certainly am!"

"Are you and Jimmy Don going steady?" asked Lucinda. Lu felt that in view of their long, close friendship, she was entitled to ask Tommie personal questions.

"No," answered Tommie. "He's free to date anyone he wants to."

"You've always refused to date anyone until he came along," observed Lucinda. "It seems to me that one time, in one of my weak moments when I let you talk about your religion, you told me Adventists don't marry outside their own church."

"Yes, I know I did," replied Tommie.

"Well, I'll bet you'd marry Jimmy Don if he asked you," Lu retorted. "I would—and so would any girl in school. He's the handsomest boy I've ever seen!"

"I don't know, Lu. I just don't know," Tommie said in such a troubled voice that Lucinda realized the question had touched on something painful. She tactfully changed the subject.

But Tommie was unable to get her conscience to change the subject. "I don't know if I'd marry him or not," she argued with herself. "Maybe he will become an Adventist. He seems so interested in what I believe. Then it would be all right. But suppose he doesn't? Would I say No in that case? I said I wouldn't accept a date with him, but I did, the very first time he asked me."

There matters stood when, shortly after the second semester of the school year started, Jimmy Don came unexpectedly to the Gordon home one evening and asked Tommie to go for a ride.

"I'm going to quit school, Doc," he explained. "You know my dad is crippled, and this last year has been pretty hard for us financially. I have a good job lined up in the northern part of the state, and I'm leaving tomorrow."

"But Jimmy, isn't there some way your family could manage until after graduation?" Tommie asked. "It's such a short time until we finish school."

"I know, but we can't seem to make it," he replied. "I promised the folks that I'd come back and finish high school when we get all straightened out." He was silent for a few minutes. Then he said, "I'll write to you as soon as I get to my job, and don't forget to mention me in your prayers."

The days were empty after Jimmy Don left, but in a way it was a relief to Tommie. Now she could think about the future without Jimmy Don there to confuse the issue. Letters passed between them regularly, and one day about a month before school closed he was back.

"I've been drafted, Doc," he explained. "I'm going into the Air Force, and I'll have only a few days at home." Before he left, he said again, "I'll write as soon as I get to wherever they send me, Doc—and don't forget to mention me in your prayers."

Tommie missed Jimmy Don terribly, but her mind was more at ease. She had not been required to make a decision as far as he was concerned. Now it seemed that such a decision would not have to be made for a long time.

The activities taking place during the last month of school were taking much of Tommie's time—class parties, skip day, and graduation plans. Tommie was valedictorian, just as her classmates had predicted at the beginning of school, and she worked hard on her speech for graduation night.

Letters came from Jimmy Don. Finally one said, "Doc, do you mind if I write to some of the other girls in the class too? Mail is very important to us; we get awfully lonesome. If you'd rather I didn't, I won't, because you are the one who is really important to me."

"Of course I don't mind if you write to the other girls," she wrote in return, but she knew that wasn't true. "I do mind, terribly, but I have no right to be jealous," she thought. "I have to admit that I am in love with him and want to marry him, but I dread for him to ask me. I don't know whether I'd marry him or not. At least I wouldn't until I was through nurses' training—I think."

Graduation day arrived, and in the mail came a package for Tommie. She had received numerous other graduation gifts, but this one was special—it was from Jimmy Don. Inside the package was a picture of Jimmy in his Air Force uniform. There was also a locket containing a smaller picture of him.

Tommie couldn't remember whether or not she had ever mentioned to Jimmy Don that Adventists don't wear jewelry, but she whispered, "I'll wear it anyway, just for tonight. Then I'll put it away and never wear it again."

That evening the seniors marched in proudly, wearing their maroon caps and gowns, and the program began. There was the usual reading of the class history, the class will (Tommie had bequeathed her freckles to a boy in the junior class who had even more than she did), and the class prophecy which predicted great things from the thirteen young people sitting on the platform.

Reatha finished her speech as salutatorian, and it was Tommie's turn. She caught her breath as the applause of the community greeted her. Then she lifted her head and began the speech she had written and practiced so faithfully: "Members of the school board, teachers, parents, classmates, and friends—"

When the program was over, Tommie was surrounded by neighbors and friends. "Fine speech, Tommie!" "Congratulations, Tommie!" "We're proud of you, young lady!" "We hear you're going into nursing. Good luck!"

Tommie worked her way through the crowd to where her parents stood. "Did I do all right?" she asked them anxiously. "Could you hear me when I spoke?"

"We never heard a word you said," her father replied. "We sat at the back of the gymnasium by the open doors, and a little dog outside was having a running fit. We got so interested in watching the dog we never heard a word of your speech!"

Tommie recoiled as if she had been struck and swallowed hard to keep back the tears. For an aching moment she wished desperately that Jimmy Don had been there; he had been so proud of her for being valedictorian. If there had only been someone who really cared, it would have made a big difference. Even Mamma had changed in the past two years, as if the struggle to defend Tommie against her father's opposition had been too much for her.

Muttering something about returning her cap and gown, Tommie walked away. Then she went to sit in Uncle Bill's car. There she shed a few quiet tears as she waited for the rest of the family to come. Again she longed for the one person she felt would have understood what the evening meant to her.

That night Tommie carefully placed her diploma in a box that contained all her treasures and keepsakes. In the same box she placed the locket.

She paused, thoughtfully. She realized that her classmates would

51

scatter. She was sure she had seen some of them for the last time. When September came she would join a new class, form new loyalties, and in turn say good-bye to them.

In the meantime she could enjoy a summer at home. She sighed and dropped to her knees beside her bed for evening prayers, not forgetting to mention Jimmy Don.

Tommie's application to enter nurses' training had been accepted. Now it was only a matter of time and money. Time was running short—classes would start in two weeks; and so far the fifty dollars she needed for entrance fee had not come from any source. She made it a matter of prayer and packed her suitcase to show her faith.

One evening Mr. Pender from the neighboring farm stopped for a visit.

"Well, Tommie, are you all set for nurses' training?" he asked.

"Yes, almost," Tommie replied.

"What do you mean—'almost'?" he queried. "Isn't it all settled?"

"All but my entrance money," came Tommie's answer. "I don't have that yet."

"How much is it?"

"Fifty dollars," Tommie said.

"I wouldn't worry about it," he said comfortingly. "Your daddy can afford to let you have that money."

Tommie's father spoke up. "I could probably afford it, all right, but I'm not going to give it to her. I don't want her to be a nurse, and I won't help her in any way if she persists in going ahead with her plans. You see, my sister was a nurse, and during that flu epidemic in 1918 I used to go with her into homes and help her. The sights she was called upon to see and the things she had to do—well, they were just awful, and I made up my mind right then that I'd never let a girl of mine be a nurse."

"I see," Mr. Pender murmured thoughtfully, and the talk turned to other matters.

After a while Daddy excused himself, saying, "I have a melon out in the spring getting cold. I'll go out and get it and we'll have some."

When Daddy had gone out the door Mr. Pender turned to Tommie and asked, "When do your classes start?"

"Two weeks from tomorrow,'" Tommie answered.

"Well, don't worry about that money. If your daddy doesn't break down and give it to you, I'll get it for you myself."

Tommie could barely stammer out her gratitude before Daddy came in with the melon. She knew she couldn't accept Mr. Pender's money. He was no better off financially than any of the others in the community, and he'd probably have to borrow the money for her. However, his interest and faith in her meant far more than fifty dollars.

Two days later Tommie received a letter from Aunt Nola—and the contents proved to be the answer to her prayers.

Aunt Nola wrote that she had accepted a job teaching in a grade school less than a hundred miles from Tommie's home, and would be leaving for there three or four days after Tommie's classes started. However, she had paid Tommie's entrance fee and would send Tommie a small allowance each month until she finished training. Besides that, she had arranged for Tommie's transportation to the hospital. Here Tommie realized with a start that she had not once, in her worry about the entrance fee, given a thought to how she would pay her fare to the hospital. "But God knew," she said to herself. "He never overlooks anything!"

Aunt Nola said that Miss Barton, the nursing instructor from the hospital, would drive through Fallton on her way back from her vacation, and if Tommie would meet her there, she could travel to the hospital with her. Miss Barton wanted to get to the hospital five days before classes started, so she'd be leaving in six days.

Further news stated that Aunt Marty was going to be the house-mother in the dormitory, and a roommate had already been picked for Tommie.

"All things work together for good—" quoted Tommie. "I think that's my favorite text. It has been proved so many times in my life. Now that everything has been taken care of, I can enjoy these last few days at home. But first, I'd better answer Aunt Nola's letter and write to Jimmy Don about it, giving him my new address."

During the next six days Tommie wandered about the farm, storing up memories to last through the next year. The farm would never really be home again. She would come back again for vacations, but that would be all. At least, this wouldn't be the first time she'd been away from home, she reminded herself. That made it easier to go.

Aunt Nola had assured Tommie that she'd like Miss Barton, and when Tommie met her at Fallton as had been arranged, she knew Aunt Nola was right. Tommie had always liked her teachers, and during the summer she had wondered what her teachers in nurses' training would be like. It would be her first experience in a Christian school. Now, looking at Miss Barton, Tommie instinctively felt that here was a person who held the highest of ideals, both as a teacher and as a human being.

"Oh, Aunt Marty, isn't it wonderful," exclaimed Tommie. Miss Barton had deposited the girl and her luggage in the dormitory a scant quarter of an hour before, and now Tommie was fairly dancing up and down with joy.

"Calm down, Tommie, or you're going to explode," cautioned her aunt.

"I'll try, only this minute it hit me that I'm really here, ready to be a student nurse, and all sorts of new experiences are ahead, and new friends too!"

"I know an antidote for that," laughed her aunt. "I'll show you to your room and you can put your things away. A little work will settle you down!"

"Who is to be my roommate?" Tommie asked as she carried her luggage down the hall behind Aunt Marty.

"Her name is Elise Shore," replied Aunt Marty. "She is a little older than you. She has been working here as an aide for several months. Here's the room you'll be living in. Just put your things away, and we'll go up to supper. If we don't meet Elise in the cafeteria you'll meet her when she gets off duty."

Aunt Marty sat on the bed and talked as Tommie put her things away. Tommie's hair had grown, and she had braided it into two braids that hung down her back, and now Aunt Marty mentioned it.

"Aunt Nola has made an appointment for you to have a permanent tomorrow, Tommie," she said. "Short hair will be much easier for you to keep tidy. You know the hospital rules are that you are to keep your hair in one roll around your head and wear a hairnet."

"Yes, I remember," responded Tommie.

"There will be some work for you to do during the few days before classes start," Aunt Marty went on, "but you won't have to work tomorrow. In the morning you'll be fitted for your student uniforms, and then you'll get your permanent. That won't leave much of the morning. During the afternoon you may rest or get acquainted with

55

the girls who aren't on duty. Now, if you're finished, we can go to supper."

As they seated themselves in the dining room, Aunt Marty took a hasty glance around and reported, "Elise isn't here, but here comes a girl who is going to be a member of your class!"

"Why, it's Anne," exclaimed Tommie, as a petite brunette sat down at the table with them.

"Hey, Tommie," greeted Anne. "We're going to be classmates. Aren't you excited?"

"I certainly am," answered Tommie. "I didn't know you were going to be in the class!"

"Your Aunt Nola told me you were coming," said Anne, "so I promised that you and I would sing a duet at Young People's Meeting on Friday night!" She giggled.

"You'd better un-promise in a hurry, then," declared Tommie firmly, "because something awful happens when you and I sing together."

"You mean, like a CATastrophe?" suggested Anne.

Tommie groaned. "Oh, what an awful pun! But yes, that is something like I had in mind!"

"I was only teasing," said Anne. "But someday I will get you up there to sing again with me, if only to prove that lightning doesn't strike twice in the same place. After all, there hasn't been a cat in church since you left."

"We'll see. We'll see," answered Tommie. "Suppose I turn out to be irresistible to cats—like catnip?"

"I never heard of anyone with a catnip personality," rejoined Anne. "Have you, Mrs. Perry?" She turned to Aunt Marty, who had been enjoying the girls' banter.

"No, I don't believe I ever did," Aunt Marty answered.

Just then Tommie felt a hand on her shoulder, and looking up, saw Miss Croft, the superintendent of nurses, standing beside her. Remembering that students and aides always stood in the presence of a doctor or supervisor, she started to rise, but the firm hand on her shoulder prevented her.

"No, don't get up, please," said Miss Croft. "And be seated, Miss Bond," she added to Anne who was already on her feet. "I just came by to welcome you to the hospital, Miss Gordon, and to tell you that we're glad to have you in our freshman class."

"Thank you," smiled Tommie. Secretly Tommie was very much in awe of the lovely superintendent of nurses. She was so—so— Tommie groped for the right word. Regal! That was it. "She's so gracious and serene. I'd like to be just like her. She's an ideal nurse," Tommie thought as she watched Miss Croft leave the dining room.

Back in Aunt Marty's room Tommie asked, "How many members of the freshman class are already here?"

"Four," replied Aunt Marty.

"I've met Anne, I know Elise is here, and I make the third one. Who is the fourth one?"

"Heidi Parker is living in the dormitory too. She works for the business manager's wife," said Aunt Marty. "She will be here any-time now."

A few moments later two faces appeared at the door, and two voices spoke simultaneously.

"Is this our new classmate?"

"Is this my new roommate?"

Tommie looked up. One girl was slender, brown-eyed, with hair that was already graying. That would be Elise, Tommie guessed. And the other girl, merry-faced and slightly plump, must be Heidi. Introductions were made, and at that moment Anne came in.

Elise took Tommie's hand in hers and said, "Come on, roommate— let's invite the other classmates down to our room for a visit. We can get acquainted that way and leave your aunt free to manage the rest of her brood!"

Some time later Tommie laughed, "I'll bet we sound like a flock of birds, the way we've been talking."

"I expect we do," agreed Heidi. She lifted one of Tommie's braids. "I love these pigtails of yours, Tommie," she said. "They make you look not a day over thirteen!"

"Then it's a good thing I'm having them cut off tomorrow," said Tommie. "We can't have the patients thinking that mere children are caring for them."

"If you're going to have them cut off tomorrow, I'd better get my camera out right now," said Elise. "I want your picture while you still have these braids."

Tommie obediently posed for the picture; then the four went up to the chapel for evening worship.

Elise was already on duty when Aunt Nola awakened Tommie for breakfast the next morning. The morning went hurriedly by and

Tommie was free. Her head felt oddly light without the heavy braids. She hoped the short hairdo made her look older. Tommie felt it was a distinct disadvantage to look so much younger than her years, but Mamma always said, "The older you get the more you'll appreciate looking younger!"

"I'd better catch up on my letter writing," Tommie decided. "Later I won't have so much time."

She had promised Mamma to write as soon as she arrived at the hospital, so that was the first letter to be written. She knew that letters from her mother would be a great comfort to her now that she was going to be gone a whole year.

There was a note to be written to Lucinda, who was working in a store close to her home, and a letter to Viola, who was leaving for Washington, D.C., the next week to work as a typist.

There had to be a letter to Jimmy Don, of course, but she decided to do that after supper. Anne had said she would have two hours off that afternoon, so she and Tommie planned to take a walk, maybe even go all the way into town.

Shortly after three o'clock Anne came hurrying down the hill. "Ready, Tommie?" she asked as she paused in Tommie's doorway.

"I'm ready," replied Tommie.

"I'll change my clothes; it will take only a minute," said Anne, and popped into her own room just across the hall from Tommie's.

As the girls sauntered along the street, Tommie asked, "Have you seen Janet lately, Anne?"

"Not for almost a year," replied Anne. "Maybe she will come to see you before long. She lives only forty miles away."

"I wrote her that I was coming to take training and when I'd be here," said Tommie. "I'd just love to see her."

The two hours went by quickly. "Suppertime," announced Anne. "Let's hurry to the cafeteria before it gets crowded. Besides, I want to see if I have any mail. I haven't heard from my boyfriend for a long time. He's in the Army."

"I can't expect any mail just yet," said Tommie, "since I arrived only yesterday," but she waited as Anne sorted through the mail. Anne slipped one envelope into her pocket. "Oh, you got a letter, Anne. I'm glad."

"Oh, it isn't mine," Anne explained. "It's written to a friend of mine, but since she came only yesterday and can't expect any mail yet, I'll keep it for her until she does expect it!"

58

Tommie snatched the letter from Anne's pocket. Sure enough, it was addressed to Miss Tommie Gordon," and the handwriting was Jimmy Don's!

"From your boyfriend, isn't it?" smiled Anne.

"Yes," admitted Tommie. "He's in the Air Force in New Mexico right now."

"Not in the medics?" queried Anne.

"He's not—an Adventist," replied Tommie in a low voice.

"My boyfriend isn't either," confessed Anne.

Heidi's arrival stopped the conversation at that point, and the three girls went on to supper.

The next day Tommie worked in the hospital kitchen, drying dishes while some of the kitchen equipment was being repaired. The young girl who helped her introduced herself as Jenny Cobb.

"I'm going to be a nurse's aide as soon as there's an opening for one," she said, "but now I'm having to work in the kitchen."

"I'm going to be a member of the freshman class," Tommie said. "We'll probably be working together again one of these days when you are an aide and I'm a student nurse."

"I'm going to work here only until I get married—as soon as my boyfriend gets out of the Army," said Jenny.

That evening when Tommie got back to the dormitory she found two more class members had arrived. They were Betty and Nellie. Now there were six freshmen on the campus.

The next day Betty, Nellie, and Tommie were set to work dusting books and washing shelves in the library. That day several more freshman students arrived. And the following day the rest came.

The evening before classes started, the girls drifted out by ones and twos and soon found themselves seated in a large circle on the lawn. Then one girl who displayed the sure characteristics of a born leader stood up and said, "We may as well get acquainted. After all, we hope to spend three years together. I'll start. I'm Marjorie Wendell, commonly known as 'Wendy'; I'm from Illinois, and unlike many of you, I've had no experience in hospital work at all. I've always wanted to be a nurse, though, so here I am." Then, pointing to the girl seated beside her, she announced, "You're next!"

As the girls stood one by one and told about themselves, Tommie began to get an idea of the diversity of the parts that made up the whole. The girls came from Illinois, Wisconsin, Virginia, North

Carolina, Oregon, Missouri, Michigan, New York, Tennessee, and other states. They ranged in age from seventeen-year-old Lucille to Elise, who was thirty-six. Some, like Tommie, were just out of high school or academy, while others had finished college and had worked awhile. There were blonds, brunettes, and red-heads. There were girls who smiled easily and others whose expressions were grave and thoughtful.

"My class!" thought Tommie. "We'll go through a lot together, and some of us won't make it through. By the grace of God I intend to stick it through to the end of this course, if it is His will that I be a nurse!"

All at once she was aware that Wendy's finger was leveled at her, and Wendy's crisp voice was saying, "You're next!"

Tommie arose. "I'm Tommie Gordon—" she began.

Freshman Days | 10

The next few days were bewildering even to those who had been nurse's aides in the hospital. One by one the girls were measured for their uniforms. The class schedule was posted, and armloads of books were issued.

The first day after classes the girls gathered in little groups to talk over their first impressions of the profession they had chosen.

"Just look at the size of this anatomy book," groaned Babs. "Do you suppose we'll ever be able to learn even a part of it?"

"Nursing arts class sounds interesting," said Fran. "I'll feel I'm on my way to becoming a nurse when I've been taught to take temperatures and give baths."

"Well, there's at least one class I don't have to worry about!" declared Tina.

"Which one is that?" asked Anne.

"Bible Doctrines," replied Tina. "I had that in academy."

"So did I," came the comment from several other girls.

Suddenly Tommie realized that she was the only one out of the class who came from a non-Adventist home. Bible Doctrines class might not be hard for the rest, but she would have to study just as hard on that course as she would for any of the others.

"Isn't Miss Croft a dear?" said Betty. "She's my ideal. I want to be just like her."

Tommie smiled to hear Betty express the very thoughts she'd had about Miss Croft. "I'm going to enjoy her medical ethics class, I think. Of course, I did learn some of that when I was a nurse's aide."

"Now, why do we have to take Progressive Classwork?" demanded Wendy. "That's for little kids."

Tommie had no idea what Progressive Classwork was until Carol spoke up. "Most of us have already taken Friend and Companion, and a lot of us have passed Guide. We'll probably work on the Master

61

Guide requirements, and that isn't for little kids. That's a real challenge to adults."

Now Tommie understood. Miss Ruby, the record librarian, had helped her through the Friend and Companion requirements when she'd been a nurse's aide.

"But I don't care for things like that," insisted Wendy. "What has hiking and birds and trees and such things to do with nursing?"

"We don't want to have lopsided personalities, Wendy. We won't be good nurses if nursing is all we know," spoke up Anne.

"And it's a requirement for graduation, Wendy," added Heidi. "You'll have to be a Master Guide before you are allowed to graduate."

"Then I'll learn it, but I won't like it," declared Wendy.

"Liking it isn't required," grinned Heidi, "but it helps if you do."

"I'll be glad when we get our uniforms," said Babs.

"So will I," agreed Nellie. "I don't think I'll ever learn to tie that black tie, though."

"You'll be taught how," said Anne. "You'll find it isn't as hard as it looks."

One of the junior students made her way through the groups to the bulletin board and tacked up a notice. It read:

> "All Freshmen Students Are to Meet at the
> Fireplace at 6:30 Thursday Morning for
> Breakfast.
> > "Signed: Ruby Davis."

Everyone crowded around to read and comment.

"Those lucky freshmen," said a senior student in sham envy.

"Miss Ruby's breakfasts are really something," said a junior student to Tommie. "Her pancakes are out of this world."

"A cookout!" exclaimed Wendy. "I like cookouts."

"How could you like it?" asked Heidi. "That's part of the Progressive Classwork program."

"I didn't say I wouldn't like any of it," Wendy defended herself. "I'm just against it in general."

Aunt Marty came into the hall. "Study period, girls," she announced, and within minutes the dormitory was quiet.

One by one the girls received their uniforms and proudly wore them to class. The classes settled into their regular pattern, and the girls began to find more time for other things as their study habits improved.

Tommie studied hardest on her Bible lessons, even though they weren't as hard as she had anticipated.

Before many weeks had passed, Tommie, Anne, and Elise found their names on the list to give evening care to the patients. Since all three had been nurse's aides before entering training, they were the first to give patient care.

Then, first an hour a day, then two, the students began work in the hospital. Sometimes they washed equipment or counted and packaged sponges in surgery, but little by little they took their places and fulfilled their roles in caring for the patients.

Shortly before Christmas Tommie was hurrying down the hill from the hospital when she heard Anne behind her, calling, "Tommie! Tommie! Wait up a minute!"

Tommie stopped, and Anne caught up with her. "Here's a letter for you, Tommie," Anne panted. "It came in the evening mail. I saw you hadn't picked it up, so I brought it along. I hope you don't mind."

"I'm glad you did," said Tommie. "Thanks, Anne. I don't know how I happened to overlook it when I went through the mail. It's an important letter too," she added with a smile.

"So I noticed," said Anne.

In the seclusion of her room Tommie opened Jimmy Don's letter. She hadn't read very far before she saw that the decision she had been sure was far in the future would have to be made immediately.

Jimmy Don was asking her to marry him. He was willing to wait until she finished her nurses' training if she insisted, but he wanted to know right away if she would marry him. He was to have a short furlough at home and then be sent overseas. He wanted to know her answer before he left the States. "I'll study your religion some more, since it means so much to you; but of course I can't promise more than that," he wrote.

When Tommie picked up her pen to answer Jimmy's letter, she found that for all her seeming indecision, there hadn't been any real doubt as to whether or not she'd marry Jimmy Don. Of course she would. Love would be enough; they'd work it out. They would be the exception to the rule. And hadn't he said he'd study her religion? So Tommie wrote the letter and accepted Jimmy Don's proposal.

Slipping across the hall during study period, Tommie told Anne what the letter had contained and her own response to it. Anne put her arms around her and whispered, "It'll work out, Tommie, just the same as it will with Ben and me! We'll show them."

Comforted by Anne's encouragement, Tommie slipped back into her own room. She was glad Elise was acting as monitor on the second floor that night and hadn't been there when she read the letter. She didn't intend to tell Elise of her engagement; Elise would try to point out all the reasons why it shouldn't be, and Elise just didn't understand. Tommie decided not to tell anyone else about it, either, except Mamma. Jimmy Don would be home on furlough, and he could tell their friends.

Jimmy Don wrote once while he was home, telling her it would be some time before she received his next letter. As usual, he asked her to pray for him.

Lucinda's letter came a week later. "I saw your boyfriend, Jimmy Don, when he was home on furlough. He really lived it up, drunk every day, I heard. At least he was drunk both times I saw him. You are well rid of that one, Tommie," the letter said in part.

"I will not cry! I will not cry!" Tommie found herself repeating. "I don't believe it, anyway. There's a mistake somewhere. Perhaps it's a joke. Maybe Jimmy Don told Lu that we were engaged, and she is teasing me." Down deep inside, though, Tommie knew Lu didn't go in for jokes of that type. Lu didn't know of the engagement. Tommie knew she was just passing on a piece of news about a mutual friend. Tommie knew, too, that there had been whispers of that sort of thing while she and Jimmy Don were still in high school—whispers she had pretended to ignore. "I still don't believe it," she insisted loyally to herself. "When I get his address I'll write and ask him point-blank if he drinks! If he says he does, even a little, then I won't marry him. I'd never be able to tolerate a drunken husband, no matter how charming and handsome he is when he is sober."

The capping ceremony was in January. The class had gained two new members, Jean and Rita, who had come a month late, so now there were twenty-three members. It was an impressive ceremony. Each girl was capped by a senior student.

Tommie was on night duty that month, along with Lucille. After the ceremony the two girls dashed up the hill to the hospital, each trying to be the first to wear her cap on duty. Lucile won the race and stood inside the door, laughing as Tommie came running in a few seconds behind her. Night duty at this stage in training consisted of working until ten o'clock in the evening, and it was already nine fifteen.

"We're the first ones," Lucille generously included Tommie in her statement, although she was really *the* first one, "even if it is for only forty-five minutes."

"You look like a proper student nurse, Miss Wayland," Tommie complimented Lucille.

"And so do you, Miss Gordon!" Lucille returned the compliment. Then both girls turned and hurried into the utility room to look in the mirror and see for themselves if the caps really added to their stature as nurses. There was no doubt about it. The cap *makes* the nurse what she is, they both agreed.

At that point the door to the utility room opened, and their stood Mrs. Sorensen.

"*Humpf!*" she humpfed. "I might have known you two would be in here admiring yourselves. Every year for the past nine years, since I first came to work here, on the night of capping I've had to come into the utility room and rout out the two students who were supposed to be helping on the floors. Never once have I found them anywhere but in here looking at themselves in the mirror!"

Tommie and Lucille, blushing furiously, meekly followed Mrs. Sorensen out of the utility room and were model student nurses until they went off duty at ten o'clock.

As soon as Tommie received a letter from Jimmy Don telling her his new address, she wrote and asked him outright if he'd been drinking while he was home on furlough. His answer was reassuring.

He wrote, "I suppose you got that story from Lucinda. I realized later she would tell you and that you'd ask me about it. The truth is, Tommie, I only pretended to be drunk, both times I saw her. It was just a joke, one that wasn't very nice, I'll admit, but it *was* only a joke. You don't have to worry, dear. I don't drink, and I never intend to start."

Tommie breathed a sigh of relief. This had burdened her more than she had realized.

"Miss Gordon, will you please stay for a few minutes after Bible class today?" Elder McGee asked as Tommie entered the classroom.

"Yes, of course," she replied. "Now, why does he want me to stay after class?" she wondered. "Surely my classwork has been all right. I'm getting good grades. I'll have to wait and see, I guess."

65

When the rest of the students had filed out after class, Tommie looked inquiringly at Elder McGee.

"Miss Gordon, would you like to study our church doctrines more fully?" he asked. "Your aunts have told me about your experiences and led me to think you'd like to become an Adventist."

"Oh, I would! I would!" exclaimed Tommie, her face alight.

"You've done fine work in class, and I don't think you'll need much further instruction," the minister said. "If you come to the parsonage at four o'clock this afternoon, we'll arrange your studies."

At five o'clock that afternoon Elder McGee leaned back in his chair and smiled at Tommie. "Miss Gordon," he said, "none of us expected you to be this well-grounded in the message. You don't need studies."

"I've studied hard all along," Tommie said, "because I wanted to be sure of what I was doing. You think I am ready to be baptized, then, Elder McGee?"

"I certainly do," he replied. "I'm going to make a call this coming Sabbath, and the baptism will be the following Sabbath. There will be at least one other person being baptized besides you."

The day of Tommie's baptism came. It was her Sabbath to work the morning shift and get off at one o'clock in the afternoon, but Miss Croft had arranged for her to get off duty for the church service. As Tommie neared the church she met Fran going back up to the hospital.

"Tommie, there's a girl down there looking for you. She has the prettiest blond hair and the cutest dimples," Fran said.

"It must be Janet," exclaimed Tommie. "Thanks for telling me, Fran." And Tommie hurried on.

Janet met Tommie just outside the door and threw her arms around her.

"Oh, Tommie, it's so good to see you!" Janet stepped back and took a good look at her. "Same old Tommie, aren't you? Are you off duty this afternoon so we can talk?"

"I'll get off at one o'clock," Tommie laughed. "Oh, Janet, won't it be fun to visit again? I've a million questions I want to ask you. And, oh, Janet, I'm so glad you picked today to come. I'm going to be baptized today!"

In shocked surprise Tommie saw the warmth and light die out of Janet's face.

"But—but Janet—aren't you glad?" she stuttered.

"No, I'm not," retorted Janet shortly. "Now you won't be any fun.

You'll go all religious on me and won't laugh or joke or anything."

"Why, that's the silliest thing I ever heard of," declared Tommie. "I've never been ashamed of being happy, and I don't expect that to change just because I'm being baptized. Come on, now," she coaxed, "come on in and be happy with me."

Janet let herself be led into the church, but Tommie was aware of her resentment and was puzzled by it. Then it was time for the baptism, and Tommie forgot Janet, remembering only that she was publicly showing her determination to follow the Lord.

Immediately after church Janet said to Tommie, "I'm going to be down at the dormitory. Stop by when you get off duty."

When one o'clock finally came, Tommie fairly flew down the hill, hoping she had misunderstood Janet's attitude that morning. Janet was in the dormitory parlor visiting with Heidi, who was from the same town as Janet was. As Tommie paused in the doorway, Janet smiled her dimpled smile and said, "Come on in, Tommie, and sit down here by me. And please don't mind how I acted this morning. I was so afraid you'd go religious and wouldn't approve of me anymore, but I was talking to Anne, and she told me you were engaged, and to a non-Adventist, at that, so I guess you really can't be too religious!"

Tommie turned her face away, in her heart a soundless cry: "Dear Lord, what have I done? I didn't realize the example I was setting. All right, Lord, I'll give him up—only, not yet, Lord—please, not yet."

"Tommie," Janet prattled on, "I was just telling Heidi about my date last Saturday night."

"With Johnny Hazen, I presume?" said Tommie.

"Not that character," Janet sniffed disdainfully. "I left him behind a long time ago. He wasn't any fun anymore. Every time I'd suggest going to a good movie or having a coke or something like that, he'd preach at me. Finally I got acquainted with some of the boys there in town, and now I'm really living. They know how to give a girl a good time, and no preaching, either."

Tommie began to understand Janet's earlier attitude a little better. As Janet talked on, telling of her escapades and so-called good times, Tommie found it hard to believe that this was the same Janet who had helped her so carefully along the Christian pathway. The blue eyes sparkled as brightly as ever, the smile was still as beguiling, the dimples still as attractive; but the Janet Tommie remembered would never have let such slang pass her lips. There was no doubt about it; Janet had greatly changed.

67

Heidi had excused herself and gone, and now Tommie and Janet were alone in the parlor. During a pause in one of Janet's narratives, Tommie asked, "Are you really having a happy life, Janet?"

"I should say I am," Janet declared. "I never knew what real living was before."

Tommie took one of Janet's hands in hers as she asked, "Would you recommend that kind of life for me, Janet?"

Janet was silent for a moment and then answered in a low voice, "No, Tommie. You're different from me. You wouldn't be happy." In a still lower voice she added, "And maybe I won't always be happy with it, either!" Then, raising her head, she said, "Anyway, I've been doing all the talking, Tommie. Now, tell me how you like nurses' training."

That evening as Janet left, she again put her arms around Tommie and said, "I'll see you again, Tommie, I don't know exactly when. But in the meantime, don't change—please don't!"

Vacation | 11

The notice on the bulletin board read, "Please place your name under your vacation preference." Tommie unhesitatingly placed hers under "June 1 to 15." She was anxious to get home. Elise wasn't going until the middle of July, and Anne had asked for June 8 to 22.

A few days before vacation started, Miss Barton found Tommie working on second floor and said to her, "Miss Gordon, you'll be welcome to ride part way to your home with me, if you like, at least as far as Fallton. I'm going to leave the morning of June first, as close to six o'clock as possible."

"Thank you, Miss Barton, I'd love to ride with you," Tommie answered gratefully. It was an answer to prayer. Tommie had saved enough money for a bus ticket home, but she'd had no assurance that she'd be able to get money for the return trip.

The night before her vacation started, someone rapped softly on Tommie's door after lights were out. "It's me—Carol," came a voice.

"Come on in, Carol," whispered Tommie.

"I came to say good-bye, Tommie," Carol said. She sat down on Elise's bed. "I'm leaving early in the morning."

"Then have a nice vacation," said Tommie. "We'll be getting back about the same time, too."

"I'm not coming back," answered Carol.

"Not coming back?" asked Tommie, astonished. "You mean you are dropping out of training?"

"I never did really want to be a nurse," Carol explained. "I taught school for two years and loved it, and now I'm going back to teaching. My parents always wanted me to be a nurse, but this whole year I've felt that I was wasting time!"

"I understand," said Tommie. "I guess it's better to drop out now before you waste more time. But you know we'll miss you!"

"I'll miss all of you too. And even if I do quit, I'll still feel a part of the class," said Carol.

"You'll always *be* a part of the class," responded Tommie. "Now don't forget to write to us and tell us how things go with you."

"I will," promised Carol. "Good-bye, Tommie."

"Good-bye, Carol."

A few minutes later Elise came in. She had been in Aunt Marty's room during the time of Carol's visit.

"Did you say good-bye to Carol?" Tommie asked.

"Yes," replied Elise. "I met her in the hall."

"She's the first one of us to go," sighed Tommie.

"Yes," replied Elise. "And there are three others whose grades are too low to permit them to stay in training."

"Who are they?" asked Tommie.

"Sarah, Ellen, and Nancy," replied Elise. "There are always a few who can't make it scholastically. It's too bad."

"What do they plan to do?"

"Nancy is going to take a practical nurses' course. She says it will be easier. Ellen says she'll get a job of some kind, and Sarah— Well, you know Sarah. She just laughed and said that maybe she'd get married."

"When will they be leaving?" Tommie asked.

"When their scheduled vacation comes around," said Elise.

"Then I'll see them when I get back from my vacation," said Tommie.

"If you don't go to sleep you'll not wake up in time to go on vacation," reminded Elise. "Good night, Tommie!"

"Good night, Elise!"

Two days later the bus from Fallton deposited Tommie in her hometown just at dusk. She hadn't written her parents that she was coming. She wanted it to be a surprise. Now she wasn't so sure that had been wise. It would soon be dark, and she was still five miles from home.

"I can walk," she decided. "It won't be the first time I've walked home from here. Maybe I can leave my suitcase somewhere."

The grocery store was closing when Tommie walked in. "May I leave my suitcase here until morning?" she asked.

"Yes, you may," the clerk answered. "I'll put it here behind the counter."

A few minutes later Tommie was trudging down the familiar road home. At first there were lights in the homes along the way, but as time passed they became fewer and fewer. There was no moon, but Tommie had travelled that road so often she thought she could go home from town even if she were wearing a blindfold.

At last she passed the ridge-road corner. "Almost home," her heart sang.

Then she was rapping at the door and calling out, "Anybody home?"

"That's Tommie," she heard her mother say.

The lamp was lit, and Tommie sat happily answering questions. Finally Mamma said, "You had better go to bed, Tommie. We can talk all day tomorrow."

As Tommie snuggled drowsily in her own bed for the first time since the previous August, she thought, "It's a good thing I don't have this bed in my room in the dormitory. I'd never get up in the morning."

But she did get up in the morning, and after putting on a pair of her old jeans and a shirt, she wandered into the kitchen.

"Um-m-m, breakfast smells good," she exclaimed. "The cook at the hospital is first-rate, but she can't make biscuits and gravy the way you can, Mamma."

Mamma smiled. "I made an extra pan of biscuits this morning. I thought you'd be hungry after that walk you took last night."

"Grand! Now what is planned for this morning?"

"We're going to pick beans," Mamma answered, "but you don't have to help. You may come to the field if you want to. Mrs. Hankins and the two boys are going to pick for us today."

"I can pick too," Tommie declared. "I'm out of practice, but I'll try."

As the morning wore on, Tommie realized how unaccustomed her muscles were to this kind of work. More and more often she had to straighten up and rest her aching back. She was glad when Mamma asked her to go to the house to help cook dinner.

As they worked in the cool kitchen, Mamma snapping beans and Tommie peeling potatoes, Mamma said hesitantly, "Tommie, I've been thinking about your engagement to Jimmy Don. I've never written to you how I feel, but Tommie, I think it's all wrong. You and Jimmy Don wouldn't have a happy marriage!"

Tommie looked up, startled at her mother's words. "But why, Mamma?"

"Because of your religion, Tommie. I'm against your marrying Jimmy Don more for his sake than for yours. I know what it means to be married to an Adventist. Your daddy had left the Adventist Church long before I met him, but he retained enough of his Adventist beliefs to make me miserable. I loved to dance, use makeup and jewelry, and go to movies and parties. I still see nothing wrong with those things, but your daddy never allowed me to do any of them. On the other hand, he saw to it that I couldn't go to church, either. Tommie, I don't believe that an Adventist should marry anyone who isn't a member of that church."

"Jimmy Don has promised to study my religion, Mamma," Tommie said slowly. "If he accepts it, that will end the problem. If he doesn't— Well, I've not thought what I'll do in that case."

"If Jimmy Don accepts your religion just so you'll marry him, you'll still have problems," persisted Mamma.

"I know," answered Tommie, "but I am sure I'll know if he is sincere about accepting it."

"I hope so," Mamma said doubtfully. "Well, you have another two years before you have to decide, and Jimmy Don is apt to be overseas at least that long. Maybe I'm crossing my bridges before I come to them. Still, I wanted you to know how I feel."

Tommie was grateful that the rest of the family came in just then. She considered that the conversation was getting uncomfortable. She had expected no opposition from her family, and here was Mamma set against her marrying a non-Adventist. On the other hand, Anne, who was an Adventist, seemed to think that Tommie and Jimmy Don could work things out with practically no trouble. It was confusing, to say the least.

A couple of days later Mamma said, "Granny and Grandpa want you to spend a few days with them while you're home, so if you'd like, we'll all go up there tomorrow and come back for you on Thursday. And Jimmy Don's mother wants you to spend a couple of days with her. While you're at Granny's I can write Laura Brewer and tell her you're home. Then she can let you know when she wants you to come."

"It sounds fine," said Tommie. "I can see Lucinda while I'm visiting Granny and Grandpa."

Granny and Grandpa were delighted to have Tommie as their guest, and wanted to hear about the things that had happened to her during the year she'd been gone. Tommie talked until she thought she would lose her voice. She seldom had such an attentive and appreciative audience.

72

In the course of her recital, she said, "And then, this spring, I was baptized."

"Into the Adventist Church?" asked Granny.

"Yes," answered Tommie.

Granny looked disappointed. "I'd always hoped you wouldn't join that church, Tommie. It's so different."

"Let me tell you what we believe, Granny, and then perhaps you won't feel so strongly opposed," Tommie responded quickly, and without waiting for Granny's assent she began to outline the beliefs of the Adventist Church. Her hard work in Bible Doctrines class came to her aid, and she felt she was answering well for her faith, when Granny interrupted.

"No more, Tommie! Don't tell me any more!"

Tommie stopped and looked at her questioningly.

Granny explained, "If I don't know all this, the Lord won't hold me responsible for it in the judgment."

"But it's all in the Bible, Granny," Tommie said. "I know you believe the Bible."

"But if it isn't pointed out to me, I won't have to worry about it," Granny answered. "I can go on to my own church as I always have and be happy. No, Tommie, I don't want to hear any more about your religion!"

"All right, Granny, I won't tell you any more," Tommie said, but she thought to herself, "I can live it, though. I guess that is all I can do as far as Granny and Grandpa are concerned."

Tommie and Lucinda had arranged to meet the next afternoon when Lucinda was through work. They walked together to the ice-cream store and sat in a booth as they talked and enjoyed their milk shakes.

"Tommie," Lucinda said, "I'm still embarrassed when I think of what I wrote you about Jimmy Don. Of course I didn't know you were engaged to him. I hope you've forgiven me."

"Oh, that," laughed Tommie. "He explained that to me, Lu. He said he just pretended to be drinking, to tease you. It was a natural mistake for you to make."

"So that was it," smiled Lucinda, but Tommie had an uneasy feeling Lucinda wasn't entirely convinced.

"She doesn't know him as well as I do," she comforted herself.

The girls finished their milk shakes, walked back to Granny's house, and continued their talk as they sat in the porch swing. It was late when they said good-bye, promising to keep corresponding as they had done during the past year.

Tommie did not go to sleep immediately that night. She lay awake, thinking of the high school classmates she and Lu had spoken of that evening. Reatha had been married shortly after school was out the year before. Viola was in Washington working as a typist for the Government. Most of the boys were in the service; Larry had been killed in the Pacific, and Fred was missing in action.

When Tommie got home the next day there was a letter from Mrs. Brewer waiting for her. She wanted Tommie to spend two days with her the next week. She would pick Tommie up and bring her home when the visit was over. After that visit, Tommy would have two more days at home before going back to the hospital.

Mrs. Brewer welcomed Tommie warmly. As they were driving away to her home she said, "I'm tickled to death, Tommie, to know that you are going to be my daughter. When Jimmy Don first started dating you, I began to hope it would lead to this, and now I can't tell you how happy it has made all of us. Did Jimmy Don tell you that the high school awarded him his diploma this year?"

"Why, no, he didn't," said Tommie. "I'm glad, though."

Mrs. Brewer chuckled. "Probably he doesn't write as much news to you as he does other things."

Tommie blushed. No, there wasn't much news in Jimmy Don's letters, but some of the poetry, she felt, was really outstanding. She preferred his poetry to any of Elizabeth Browning's works. And, too, his letters contained all sorts of plans for the future—their future.

Mrs. Brewer observed the blush and chuckled again.

Tommie had always felt at home with Jimmy Don's family. They tried to make her welcome when she arrived. Now her relationship to them was even closer—someday she would actually be a part of the family. They let her know they highly approved.

Delightful as her visit was, it had to end. As they drove onto the main road Mrs. Brewer said, "If you don't mind, Tommie, I'll stop here at the mailbox and see if I have any mail. I may have a letter from Jimmy Don."

Sure enough! When she got back in the car she handed the letter to Tommie and said, "Here, Tommie, you read it to me while I drive."

Tommie read aloud as Mrs. Brewer drove. At the end of the letter Jimmy Don wrote, "I've been sick, Mom, with some kind of liver ailment. It isn't serious and I'm out of the hospital now, but the doctor says I may have to go back in later. I didn't tell Tommie because I don't want her to worry!"

"Well, I guess we can't keep the news from you now, can we, Tommie?" Mrs. Brewer said soberly. "You can help me worry about him."

For the rest of the ride neither of them spoke, each busy with her own thoughts, and Tommie's thoughts were exceedingly bitter.

"Liver disease! Cirrhosis, of course. And cirrhosis is caused by drinking! No wonder he didn't want me to know—me, a nurse who would recognize the disease and its cause! Lucinda was right when she wrote me he'd been drinking—and he tried to pass it off as a joke. Drinking is never a joke. Well, he's in Italy now, where he can get all the drinks he wants. This is the end for Jimmy Don and me. I can't go on being engaged to him, knowing that he drinks and doesn't tell me the truth. I love him, but I have to be strong enough to give him up. When I get back to the hospital, I'll write and tell him it is over and ask him not to write again!"

Vacation was over. Tommie arrived back at the dormitory early Sabbath morning. She was more depressed than she had ever been before, and as she entered the dormitory hall she wished with every fiber of her being that she were back home. "At this late date I'm suffering from homesickness," she thought wryly.

It had been arranged that she and Anne would be roommates this coming year, and Anne had promised to move Tommie's things into her room before she left on her vacation, and put any of Tommie's mail there that came before she left.

With a flash of insight Tommie knew that if she entered that room and saw Jimmy Don's letters that were sure to be waiting, she wouldn't have the courage to break their engagement. Therefore, she sat down in the parlor and wrote the letter, leaving it up to him to break the news to his parents. Then she hurried up the hill to the hospital and mailed the letter. There would be no turning back now.

Only then did she enter the room that was now hers and Anne's. The letters were there as she had expected they would be—seven of them. Tearing them, unopened, into tiny fragments, she dropped them into the wastebasket.

Later, drying her tears, she was glad Anne still had another week of vacation. "I'll likely be hard to live with, at least for a while," she thought to herself. "Maybe by the time Anne comes back I will have gotten hold of myself to some extent. This is the most painful thing I've ever done, and it will take a while to recover. But Anne will understand—and she'll be patient."

Suddenly her eyes fell upon a letter on the floor. Someone had probably slipped it under the door after Anne had left for her vacation. Tommie picked it up. It was addressed to Anne, so she put it on Anne's dresser. Anne would be glad to hear from Ben again, Tommie knew. The writing didn't look like Ben's, but the letter had a military postmark, so it must be from him.

She heard the other girls beginning to stir and knew they would soon be popping in to welcome her back. She hurried to the bathroom and bathed her eyes in cold water to remove all traces of the tears she'd shed. She practiced a smile or two in front of the mirror before she faced her classmates.

The Unwelcome Letter | 12

Anne closed the door with the barest whisper of sound, but Tommie sat up in bed.

"Oh, roommate, I'm so glad you're back," she said in a low voice. All week it had seemed to Tommie that if she could exist until Anne got back from her vacation, she could pour out her troubles to her and things would be better.

"What's the matter? Too much work now that some of us are on vacation?" teased Anne.

"No—I've got troubles," Tommie declared ungrammatically.

Anne looked at her sharply and then came to perch on the side of the bed.

"I'm listening," she said.

When Tommie had finished her story Anne nodded seriously. "I see," she agreed. "You do have trouble. Only, the worst part is over now, isn't it?"

Tommie nodded. "I tear up his letters. You know how slow mail is now, and I'm still getting letters from—from—him, so I tear them up without reading them. I've burned up all the others I'd saved, and I sent his pictures and the locket back to him. But I keep thinking —and missing—"

"Of course," Anne said quickly. "It will take a while to get over that. But Tommie, I want you to know I think you did the right thing, and I'm proud of you. Someday—maybe—I'll be brave enough to break my engagement, but not yet!"

"It's not easy," Tommie agreed. "You remember that day I was baptized and Janet came? Well, that morning she'd been angry because I was going to be baptized, and she was afraid I'd 'go religious' and not be fun anymore, she said. That afternoon she was all smiles again. She said she knew I couldn't be too religious if I were engaged to a non-Adventist. It struck me then just what I was doing,

77

and I told the Lord that I'd give Ji—him—up, only not just yet. So you see, Anne, I know how it is. Even if you know what's right, and you think you are going to go ahead and do what's right, you keep wanting to put it off because it hurts too much!"

"Sort of like going to the dentist," observed Anne.

"Dentists give you an anesthetic," Tommie said with a ghost of a smile. "But in a case like this, the pain just keeps on. It is not as if I'd fallen in love with someone else, or didn't love Ji—him—anymore. I still do. I know I'll get over it, only—"

"You wish it would ease up a bit, is that it?" asked Anne.

"Yes, I do. And yet, Anne, I know this is nothing compared to the pain I'd have if I married him, knowing he drinks as much as he evidently does. Did I ever tell you, Anne, that my grandpa—Mamma's father—is a drunkard?"

"No, I don't think you did," replied Anne.

"Well, he is," Tommie went on. "He is one of the dearest, sweetest persons in the world when he's sober. I love him almost more than anyone else. He has never been too busy to listen to my questions or tell me stories or repeat famous speeches to me. He can say the 'Gettysburg Address' or Bryan's 'Cross of Gold' speech until I have shivers up and down my back. But when he is drunk— Well, that is a different story. He doesn't get mean or abusive. He just gets maudlin and sentimental and cries, and gives away all his money so Granny doesn't have any to buy groceries or pay the rent. And Mamma says it was that way even when she was a little girl—never enough money, although Grandpa made a good salary. He always was able to keep a good job, teaching school or surveying land."

Tommie paused and Anne commented, "I can see why you're so against drinking."

Tommie nodded and continued, "Mamma said the other children used to chase her and her sisters and brother home, yelling at them, 'Yah, yah, your daddy's drunk again! Yah, yah, your daddy's drunk again!' I don't want anything like that to happen to my children, if I ever have any."

"I don't suppose your father ever drinks, does he?" asked Anne.

"Not a drop," Tommie declared. "You see, Mamma told him the day they were married that if he ever came home drunk she'd leave him and never come back. You can understand why, of course. But I don't suppose he ever drank, even before they were married, since he grew up in an Adventist home. He—" Tommie glanced at the clock. "Oh, look at the time!" she exclaimed. "I'm on the morning care list, and it is already a quarter of six. I'd better get dressed fast."

"Do you get off at one o'clock this afternoon?" Anne asked.

Tommie's Yes was muffled as she slipped her uniform over her head.

"I have an idea for something nice we can do this afternoon," Anne said. "Let's have dinner together, and I'll tell you about it then."

"Why not tell me now?" asked Tommie.

"I'll have to get Miss Croft's permission first," replied Anne. "Besides, if you spend your time wondering what I'm cooking up, you won't have time to worry about your own problems."

"You're right," laughed Tommie. "You're a dear, Anne. This is the first time in a week I've felt like laughing, and if I don't get to work on time I'll get a scolding that will keep me from laughing another week!"

Only the necessary work was done on Sabbath, and as many students as possible were allowed to attend church. This Sabbath, however, Tommie was kept behind and sent to work on first floor. This was the first time she had been given the responsibility of a floor without an upperclassman supervisor, and although it was to be for only an hour, she felt very important. Of course, there was nothing to do but answer lights; but still, she was in charge.

"Miss Gordon, I've been sent to help you. Is there something I can do?"

Tommie looked up to see an aide.

"Why, Ginny! Ginny Cobb! How long have you been an aide?"

"Three weeks," answered Ginny. "I like it better than working in the kitchen."

"We had fun the day I worked in the kitchen, didn't we?" asked Tommie. "And to think you worked there nearly a year before you got a chance to be an aide! I'm glad you like it."

"Do you like it in training?" asked Ginny.

"Oh, yes, I do," answered Tommie. "It's hard work, but when I'm finished, I'll have my R.N."

"I'm finished with school," Ginny said. "And I'm almost through working here. My boyfriend gets out of the Army in six weeks, and we're going to be married as soon as he gets home."

Just then a light came on and Ginny went off to answer it. Tommie had been afraid that Ginny might ask her about her boyfriend, and that was a subject she didn't want to discuss, although she had told

Ginny all about him the day they had worked together in the kitchen.

"All right now, Anne, what's on the agenda for this afternoon?" Tommie asked as they sat at lunch. "Did you clear this secret project with Miss Croft?"

"Yes, I did," smiled Anne. "Have you ever been to the orphanage?"

"No, I haven't," answered Tommie, "although I know that a few of the girls go sometimes. I've just never happened to be off duty at the right time."

"Today you're in luck," Anne said. "Some of us are going to tell the children stories. It will help us get our storytelling honor."

"I'd like that," Tommie said. "I love children. I miss my own brothers and sister so much. Have you ever been over there before?"

"Twice," answered Anne. "I enjoyed it too."

As they walked down the hill after dinner Tommie asked, "Did you find your letter from Ben?"

"A letter from Ben!" exclaimed Anne. "No, I didn't. Where did you put it?"

"On your dresser with your other mail," said Tommie.

"I didn't see it. Maybe it slipped behind the dresser. C'mon, let's hurry and find it," and Anne took Tommie's hand and hurried her along.

Sure enough, the missing letter had slipped down behind the dresser. Anne promptly sat down to read it as Tommie changed her clothes.

Suddenly Tommie was surprised to hear Anne sputtering indignantly. "Why, the very idea!" Anne exclaimed. "Who does that Heidi think she is? And he needn't think I'm going to write to him either!"

Bewildered, Tommie asked, "Why, what's wrong, Anne? What has Heidi done? Surely she hasn't been trying to cause trouble between you and Ben. I know she doesn't approve of your engagement, but I don't think she'd go so far as to try to interfere between the two of you—"

"This letter isn't from Ben," Anne explained. "Heidi wrote to Joe, a friend of ours who is stationed in New Guinea, and had him get an Adventist boy, a perfect stranger, to write to me. Well, I'm not going to write to him, so there!" She dropped the letter on the floor and placed a foot on it. "I was so hoping for a letter from Ben—it's been so long." She was near tears.

Tommie picked up the letter. "Go ahead and read it," said Anne.

The writer of the letter explained that he was a tentmate of Heidi's friend, who had suggested that he write to Anne, since Anne, Joe, and Heidi had all gone to academy together. He explained that mail was important to soldiers, and he hoped that Anne would write to him. He was an Adventist, he said, a surgical technician in the medics, and signed himself "Chad Nolan."

"He sounds nice," said Tommie. "Do you mind," she asked hesitantly, "if I write to him? After all," she added wistfully, "I won't be getting much mail now."

"Go ahead and write to him; I don't care a bit," answered Anne. "I don't have any idea what sort of person Joe might pick to write to me, though."

"It doesn't matter much," Tommie said. "It isn't as if we'll ever meet or anything. When this boy gets out of the Army and goes home, he won't be lonesome anymore and our correspondence will die a natural death. And if I don't like his letters I won't have to keep on writing; I'll know what sort of person he is after he's written to me a few times—if he does write. After all, I don't have Joe to recommend me."

"If he's lonesome, he'll write. Now come on and let's get the other girls and go on to the orphanage," said Anne, and after quickly placing the letter in her dresser drawer, Tommie followed Anne out the door.

Betty and Tina were waiting for them, and their lively talk made the walk to the orphanage pleasant. Tommie had seen the cluster of buildings and wide expanse of lawn before as she'd gone to town. Now as they went through the gate and up the walk, she saw groups of children playing and talking.

"We want you to meet Miss Katie first," Betty said. "She's the orphanage nurse, and she also takes care of the babies and the little boys up to six years old."

Miss Katie was redheaded and Irish, a veritable whirlwind of energy. She and Tommie took to each other immediately.

"I think it's your freckles, my dear," Miss Katie laughed. "I have so many of my own, and you know the old saying, 'Misery loves company'!"

"May we take your boys for a while now, Miss Katie?" Betty asked.

"Please do; they'd love it," Miss Katie answered. She turned to Tommie. "I have charge of eighteen little boys, besides the three babies, and it takes so much time to attend to their physical needs I don't have a chance to give them all the love they need, and I can't play favorites. Maybe you girls can cuddle them a bit. They need it."

Looking down at the small figures surrounding her, Tommie knew it wouldn't be hard to love them.

"Come on, youngsters," sang out Tina. "Let's go for a walk and then we'll tell you some stories."

After the walk they all sat down in the recreation room, and Tina called on Tommie for the first story. Tommie hadn't expected to be called on at all, since this was her first trip to the orphanage. However, thinking frantically, she remembered a story about a teddy bear, a story her little brother Bertie used to beg for over and over. The children listened attentively as she told it, and then, when she sat down again, one little fellow crawled onto her lap and two others nestled close to her.

"What's your name?" asked the little fellow on her lap.

"Tommie," she answered.

He looked at her with solemn eyes. "That's a boy's name," he announced. "You're Miss Teddy Bear!"

"Miss Teddy Bear is a nice name. I like it. What's your name?" responded Tommie.

"Lester," replied the child. "And he's Donnie, and that one is Tim," pointing to the boys who were snuggled closest to Tommie.

"We're Miss Katie's boys," spoke up Donnie. "Do you know Miss Katie?"

"Yes, I met her this afternoon," answered Tommie. "Sh-h-h-h, now. I think Tina is going to play the piano while we sing."

In the past, groups of the student nurses had visited the orphanage and taught the children songs and finger plays, so now the youngsters sang loudly and followed the leader's actions with enthusiasm.

Time flew. Tina announced, "All right, boys! It's time to go back to Miss Katie."

"You girls don't realize how I appreciate your taking over my boys for a few hours on Saturday afternoon," Miss Katie said when the group came back. "It gives me a chance to breathe, and to polish eighteen pairs of shoes for the boys to wear to church tomorrow."

"We enjoy it as much as the boys do," said Betty. "They are darlings, every one of them."

"They put on their very best behavior for you," laughed Miss Katie. "I hope you'll come again, Tommie, when the others come."

"That's Miss Teddy Bear," Tim informed Miss Katie.

"Is it, now?" Miss Katie replied. She turned to Tommie. "The boys give a nickname to anyone they like. They seem to feel it gives them a special claim on that person."

"They objected to 'Tommie' because they say it's a boy's name," Tommie explained. "I don't mind being called 'Miss Teddy Bear,' though. I've had worse nicknames than that."

Miss Katie grinned. "Like 'Spots' and 'Freckles'?" she inquired. "Anyone with freckles has to put up with those names. I used to hate them too."

"And as soon as you get so you don't mind those names anymore, people stop applying them to you," Tommie commented.

"Come on, girls," broke in Anne. "We'll be late to supper if we don't hurry."

The little boys immediately began to clamor to walk to the gate with the girls.

"All right, boys, you may go," said Miss Katie, "but remember you are not to go one step beyond the gate, and you must hurry right back."

Surrounded by the little boys, the girls made their way slowly to the gate. Once outside, they quickened their steps, and by hurrying as fast as dignity would allow, they reached the cafeteria before it closed.

After Sabbath vespers in the hospital parlor, Tommie and Anne walked arm in arm down the hill. As was often the case when they were not in a hurry, they turned to wander down the paths in Miss Ruby's rock garden and admire the flowers.

"Tommie, the MV leader asked me again if you and I would sing next Friday night," Anne remarked.

"What did you tell him?" queried Tommie.

"I said I'd talk to you about it," answered Anne. "Come on, Tommie, don't be silly. Accidents like that can occur only once in a lifetime."

"I guess I am being silly. After all, you've sung lots of times since and nothing has happened. All right, Anne. I'll sing with you," came Tommie's slow reply. "Shall we start practicing tonight?"

"Not tonight," Anne replied. "I want to borrow a special songbook from one of the seniors, and she's on duty. There's a lovely song in the book we could learn this week. I'll get it tomorrow, and we can start then."

"All right," agreed Tommie. "Then I guess I'll go answer that letter you got."

"Go ahead," laughed Anne. "I'm going into the parlor and listen to the radio."

Tommie sat down on her bed, reread the letter Anne had refused to answer, and was soon busily writing.

Lightning Strikes Again | 13

Tommie entered the room quietly, carrying her tray of thermometers. The patient was asleep, she noticed. Placing the tray on the over-the-bed table at the foot of the bed, she gently put her hand on the lady's shoulder.

"Mrs. Beldon, I hate to wake you up, but—"

"Oh, time for temperatures again?" Mrs. Beldon asked as she opened her eyes. She yawned and stretched, and as she did so, her foot hit the edge of the tray that protruded slightly over the edge of the table. Tray, towel and thermometers went flying as Tommie stifled a gasp of dismay.

"Well, there goes three dollars of next month's allowance; six broken thermometers at fifty cents each," she thought as she scrambled about the floor retrieving the pieces. "I have a feeling this just isn't my day to shine!"

"Oh, nurse, I'm so sorry! Are they all broken?" came Mrs. Beldon's voice.

"Yes, but it isn't your fault," Tommie soothed her. "Besides, there are more in the utility room."

Mrs. Beldon nodded, satisfied, and Tommie took the broken pieces to be replaced.

She took out the floor supply book and signed a notation that she had broken six thermometers. It wasn't the first time she had broken things. It seemed to her that every month when she got her five dollars spending money from Aunt Nola she had to pay for breakage just as regularly as she paid tithe. Only this was the worst yet—six thermometers at one time.

Tommie was late finishing the temperatures, and as hard as she could work, she couldn't seem to catch up. Hastily swallowing a bit of lunch, she went back to the floor, and when it was time for her two hours off that afternoon she stayed until she was finally finished

85

with all her morning's work. She noticed she still had time for almost an hour off duty, but as she was leaving the floor, she met Miss Croft.

"Miss Gordon, would you come and help out on first floor?" Miss Croft asked. "We have just admitted a patient who needs someone to stay with him. He's Mr. Hazen. You know Mrs. Hazen—she's one of our Adventist ladies from the Dawson church."

"Yes, I know Mrs. Hazen," Tommie replied. "I'll be glad to stay with Mr. Hazen." But Tommie wasn't really glad. She was tired and cross because of the broken thermometers and because she had hurried so all morning. "I'm a fine nurse," she thought guiltily, "letting things get me so upset this way. I'm going to have to snap out of it."

She remembered how sweet Mrs. Hazen had been to her the Sabbath she and a group of other students had gone with Elder McGee to the church at Dawson.

"So you're Tommie, Janet's friend," Mrs. Hazen had said that day. "Janet has told us so much about you. She said she was there the day you were baptized."

"Yes, she was," Tommie replied. "And you must be Johnny's mother."

"Yes, I am. I wish Johnny were here to meet you, Tommie," Mrs. Hazen went on. "He still hopes Janet will come back into the church and they can go ahead with their plans. He's taken it pretty hard."

Tommie remembered that conversation now as she followed Miss Croft into the first-floor nurses' office. She wondered if Mr. Hazen were seriously ill. That question was answered almost immediately.

"Now, Miss Gordon, here's Mr. Hazen's chart. He's in room 104," said Miss Croft. "He has tubercular meningitis," she went on, "so you'll have to wear a gown, cap and mask—the regular isolation technique you've been taught for contagious cases. He is delirious, and his temperature is high. There's a tub of ice water in there. Whenever his temperature goes over 103 degrees put a wet-sheet pack on him. Take his temperature every half hour until you get it down to 103; then take it every hour unless it goes up again."

"All right, Miss Croft," responded Tommie, and she went down the hall.

Mrs. Hazen arose from her chair outside the door to her husband's room.

"Oh, it's you, Tommie. I'm glad," she said. She indicated the tall, redheaded young man beside her. "This is my son, Johnny, Tommie. Johnny, this is Tommie—you remember, Janet's friend."

"I remember. Hello, Tommie," he said shortly.

Tommie looked at him curiously. His manner bordered on rudeness. "He's probably upset and worried about his father," she decided as she entered the room.

Within minutes Tommie was busy wrapping the icy sheets around Mr. Hazen. Soon the temperature of his fever-racked body warmed the sheets and Tommie replaced them with other sheets wrung from the tub of ice water. It was hard work, but his temperature finally came below 103 degrees, and she sat down to rest. It was then that she became aware of voices beyond the door.

"—see why they sent *her* to take care of Dad," Johnny was saying.

"Why, Son, Tommie's a good nurse. Remember, Janet used to tell us about her," Mrs. Hazen said.

"She's probably just like Janet—scatterbrained and only out for fun! Why can't we get a graduate nurse to take care of Dad?" Johnny went on.

"Johnny," his mother said tiredly, "graduate nurses are scarce. Don't be bitter because Tommie was Janet's friend. After all, they were good friends before Janet changed so much, and that doesn't mean that Tommie changed as Janet did!"

"But Mom, she doesn't look a day over fourteen. How can she know what to do for anyone as sick as Dad is?" Johnny persisted.

"Son! Son!" Mrs. Hazen's voice was on the verge of breaking. "There isn't much anyone can do now for your daddy, except pray, and I imagine Tommie is doing that as she works. Hush now. Don't say any more. She'll hear you, and it will make her feel bad."

Tommie couldn't help overhearing the conversation, and she was tempted to feel hurt; but then her feelings changed to pity for the wife and son who waited and worried outside the door.

The next time Tommie took Mr. Hazen's temperature it was up again, and she began her work anew with the wet-sheet packs. Before long Mr. Hazen began to stir and mumble.

"I'm a Seventh-day Adventist," he said clearly. Mrs. Hazen heard him, and she and Johnny entered the room. Tommie remembered Janet's telling her that Johnny's father was not an Adventist, and she wondered if he had joined the church since that time.

"But I am," he insisted as if someone had denied the truth of his previous statement. It was clear that he was delirious, unaware of the figures grouped about his bed.

"Adventist—Adventist," he mumbled. "Sent my son—Adventist

7—N.C.T.

school. Wife paid tithe. Always take up—for Adventists—people say anything—against them. I'm Adventist," he went on pleadingly.

Somehow Tommie could hardly bear it. She turned her face away as the tears rolled quietly down her cheeks.

"Now, stop it, Tommie," she told herself angrily. "Nurses don't cry, you hear? Now, stop it."

Within a few minutes she had regained her composure and was glad no one had noticed. She picked up another sheet from the tub and wrung the water from it. Just then someone touched her shoulder and she looked up.

"Tommie, you won't understand why I'm saying this, but— I'm sorry," and Johnny turned and left the room.

Mrs. Hazen sat with her face in her hands, her grief too deep for tears. Finally she arose. "I think I'll go now," she said unsteadily. "I'll just leave him in the Lord's hands. Miss Croft knows where I'll be if —if I'm needed."

Tommie's prayers that afternoon were not only for Mr. Hazen. She also prayed earnestly for her own father. "If only people wouldn't put off accepting Christ," she thought. "Sometime it may be too late. A person never knows."

When the night nurse came to relieve her, Tommie felt she'd never been so tired, not even during tomato-picking time at home. As she wearily entered her room in the dormitory, Anne looked up.

"Can you practice with me now?" Anne asked.

"Practice?" Tommie repeated dully.

"Our song for Friday night," Anne explained.

Tommie shook her head. "Too tired," she mumbled. "After I've rested I'll try it." She saw the question on Anne's face. "I'll tell you about it afterwhile."

Two hours later, after she'd had a bath and a nap, Tommie was feeling much better. Study period was not necessary during the summer, so she and Anne went into the parlor to learn the new song. Afterward they sat in their room and Tommie told Anne about taking care of Mr. Hazen that afternoon. Even as she told it tears threatened to come.

"It's about the saddest thing I ever heard," said Anne. "I went to school with Johnny Hazen too, and I know something about his family." She paused a moment and then went on, "We're going to see a lot more sad things before we finish nurses' training, and after, too. I think if we get hardened to seeing other people suffer we won't be good nurses. But we do have to keep our feelings from interfering with our work. You're a better nurse for having a tender heart."

"Thank you, Anne," Tommie said. "Whatever would I do without you to keep me straightened out?"

"You'd manage to stay on your own two feet," laughed Anne. "Oh, dear," she said in dismay, "I've a letter for you in my pocket—I picked it up on the way home."

"Is it another one from Ji—him? Because if it is, I don't want to see it," Tommie answered.

"No," said Anne. "I think it is from that boy you wrote to some time ago—Chad Nolan," and she handed the letter to Tommie.

Tommie enjoyed the chatty letter and sent an answer to it right away. It was easier than she'd thought to write to someone she didn't know and would probably never meet.

The next day when Tommie went on duty, she saw that room 104 was empty. The first-floor nurse told her that Mr. Hazen had died during the night, without ever regaining consciousness.

That afternoon she was called to the nursing office and given a long talk on the importance of little things in nursing—she had forgotten to empty the pan under the ice-box and it had overflowed until the water had run out into the hall.

"Oh, dear," she thought despondently. "I'll never be a good nurse! I break things, I get upset over my patients, and then I forget to do part of my work."

When she went to supper, she found a letter from Lucinda but decided to wait until she got home to read it. She'd written and told Lucinda about her broken engagement, and if Lucinda had any comments she wanted to read them in the privacy of her own room.

Anne was waiting for her when it was time to go home.

"Let's hurry, Anne. I have a letter from Lucinda, and I want to get home and read it," Tommie said, so Anne obligingly hurried.

Lucinda's letter was full of the usual chit-chat of town news and not until the last paragraph did she mention Jimmy Don.

"So you and Jimmy Don called it quits," she wrote. "I can't say I'm sorry, Tommie. I still think he drinks a lot. Incidentally, I hear he has a medical discharge or something and is coming home before long. That hepatitis (is that spelled right?)—anyway, that liver disease he had—"

Tommie read no further. "Oh, no!" she gasped.

Anne looked up. "Why, Tommie, what's wrong?"

"Lucinda's letter. She says Jimmy Don is coming home. He didn't have cirrhosis, Anne. He had hep—hepatitis—and, oh, Anne," she half wailed, "I don't know whether to laugh or cry!"

"Cut it out, Tommie," Anne said sternly. "If you go into hysterics, I'll throw a bucket of cold water on you!"

"I won't have hysterics, Anne. I promise. It's just that I jumped to conclusions—"

"Tommie, listen to me! You've broken your engagement. Take my advice and let it stay that way. You're far better off as things are now."

"You're right, of course, Anne. Only why was I so sure he had cirrhosis? I never once thought of hepatitis or any other liver ailment. I only thought of the one that's caused by drinking. Subconsciously, I must have believed those stories I heard."

"Hold it, Tommie," Anne smiled. "Don't go delving into psychology. We don't study that until next year!"

"Anne, you can always make me laugh, no matter how bad things are," Tommie said.

"Then repay me by coming and practicing our song for Friday night," Anne retorted. And the two girls went down the hall to the parlor.

On Friday night when Anne and Tommie marched up to sing, Tommie wondered if anyone in the congregation remembered the time she and Anne had been interrupted by a cat as they sang on that same platform. Spotting a smile here and there, she saw that at least a few people remembered that fiasco.

Just before their duet had been announced Anne had nudged Tommie and whispered, "Relax, Tommie. Lightning doesn't strike twice in the same place."

Now, looking around, Tommie wasn't so sure. It was a warm summer evening, and the doors were open. A cat could come in if he wanted to.

As they sang Tommie felt something crawling on her collar. "A katydid!" she thought. "I wonder which would be more conspicuous, to let it crawl around until it flies away of its own accord, or pick it off and hold it in my hand until we're through."

Deciding on the latter course, she reached up and grasped the insect—and a lancing pain stabbed her hand! A wasp! She released it quickly, and the insect flew triumphantly to the ceiling where it clung, buzzing angrily.

Tommie dared not look up to see if anyone had noticed. She kept on singing, but she could tell her hand was swelling rapidly.

As soon as the meeting was over several of the students gathered around Tommie.

"Better get some ice at the hospital and soak that hand," advised one of the seniors.

"You let that wasp sting you and you kept right on singing—didn't miss a note. How could you do it?" demanded Tina.

"Could you tell what happened?" Tommie asked.

"Only the people on the first couple of rows could tell," Elise answered. "You were very composed about it."

Tommie and Anne got a pan of ice at the hospital and went back to the dormitory.

"Oh, dear, what a week this has been," Tommie sighed as she held her hand submerged in the ice water. "Roommate, why don't you just shoot me and put me out of my misery?"

"Oh, no! Why, do you realize, Tommie, that with you for a roommate I get twice as much nursing experience as anybody else?" Anne grinned.

"How do you figure that?" Tommie asked suspiciously.

"Well, once this week you almost had hysterics," Anne said with a sly smile. "Then a wasp sting. And now you're despondent, wanting to be shot!"

"You can't handle this despondency," Tommie retorted. "That comes under psychiatric nursing, and you said yourself that we don't study that until next year! With all the extra practice you get in nursing, you are still deficient in some branches of knowledge!"

"Prove it," giggled Anne.

"All right," laughed Tommie. "Didn't you tell me that lightning doesn't strike twice in the same place? And didn't I just prove that it sometimes does? Something awful always happens when I sing in public!"

"Yes, I guess you're right," Anne agreed. "I don't know if I dare sing again with you."

"I'm not going to give you a chance," Tommie retorted. "From now on I'll just stay back in the audience where I belong." She removed her hand from the ice water and dried it carefully. The swelling had begun to subside, and it no longer hurt unbearably.

"Let's go to bed," she said to Anne, "before anything else happens. I'm so glad tomorrow is Sabbath. It always restores my perspective and my optimism. Do you work tomorrow morning or afternoon?"

"Afternoon," replied Anne.

"So do I," said Tommie. "See, things are looking up already. We're back on the same Sabbath work schedule. Good night, Anne!"

"Good night, Tommie!"

Pitfalls and Pranks | 14

"The new freshmen are beginning to come in," Anne told Tommie at suppertime. "Two arrived this afternoon while I was off duty, and more will be here tomorrow, I hear."

"This summer has gone fast," observed Tommie. "Classes begin next week, and we'll officially be juniors. We've come a long way in the past year."

"Yes, I know," replied Anne. "It's been fun, having no classes, but there will be compensations for having school start again. Remember how in awe of the juniors we were when we arrived last year? Now there will be a new class to stand in awe of us. And we will stand in awe of the seniors!"

Tommie smiled. "I remember," she said.

"I wish we could do something unusual to celebrate—to end our summer vacation from classes," Anne said.

"What could we do?" questioned Tommie. "Have a—oh, I know! A group of singers and entertainers from that radio program 'Hoedown' will be in town Thursday night. Do you suppose we could get permission to go? I don't see anything wrong with it. They just sing American folk songs and tell jokes. We always used to listen to the program at home, and I'd love to see them in person. I've not heard them since I left home."

Anne looked doubtful. "I don't think we'll be able to get permission."

"I'll ask Aunt Marty about it," Tommie said. "We probably can't all go, but I don't see why six or seven of us can't."

Aunt Marty seemed as doubtful as Anne had been, but after Tommie had presented all her arguments in her most persuasive manner, Aunt Marty promised to speak to Miss Croft about it.

To Anne's surprise and Tommie's delight, Aunt Marty informed the girls the next day that Miss Croft had given permission for them to attend the program.

On Thursday evening Tommie, Anne, and four other classmates started out in high spirits. Aunt Marty was going along, and she had decided that they should go in the taxi. That in itself was a real treat. There was only one taxi in town, and the owner had been a patient in the hospital several times. He knew most of the nurses by name and was always glad to have them as passengers.

"Going to the 'Hoedown' program, are you?" he remarked. "I will have you there in a jiffy. I'm surprised they let you go. You don't get to go out much at night, do you?"

"This is special," Tommie explained loftily.

"Well, have a good time," he said as he let them out at the auditorium. "If you want me when the program is over, just call me."

"Thank you, we will," replied Aunt Marty, and led the girls inside. They found seats without too much difficulty, but shortly after they sat down, the auditorium began to fill. Tommie was acutely conscious of the smoke-laden atmosphere. At home she had been used to it. Daddy didn't smoke; but when the neighbors came to visit, they always smoked, and Tommie had never minded it. Now, however, after being away from it for so long, she found the smoke irritating.

Tommie cheered up when the master of ceremonies came out onstage and introduced the program. "This is going to be fun," she told herself. "It's been so long since I've even heard the 'Hoedown' group, and to see them in person will be something to write home about!"

The program began. After each number the people in the audience clapped, whistled, and yelled, but Tommie was disappointed. Surely the singers and their choice of music hadn't been that bad when she had heard them on the radio! Then the comedian came on. Tommie smiled. His quips and jokes had always delighted her.

He began his monologue, and within a few minutes Tommie felt her face flushing. His insinuations and innuendos went far beyond the limits of good taste. Tommie was sure these jokes were used only when the group was on tour. Censorship would have made it impossible for them to be used over the air.

She twisted uncomfortably in her chair. Aunt Marty glanced at her.

"May we go? Please?" Tommie asked. "I can't stand any more of this!"

"Yes, of course," replied Aunt Marty.

"Oh, this air smells good," Anne said gratefully when they were outside the building.

"I was beginning to get a headache," Tommie said. "I'm sorry, girls, that we wasted time and money coming here. It's all my fault. I had no idea it would be like this."

"It *was* pretty awful," Anne agreed.

"Are we going back in the taxi?" someone asked.

Aunt Marty stood for a moment, thinking. "No," she decided. "Let's walk back to the dormitory. That way we can clear the smoke out of our brains and try to forget the things we heard tonight."

The walk back was refreshing. Aunt Marty enlivened it by telling of some of her experiences as a student nurse. When they reached the dormitory, Tommie stopped at Aunt Marty's door.

"May I come in and talk awhile?"

"Yes, of course," answered Aunt Marty. "I thought you might want to."

"Wasn't that program terrible?" exclaimed Tommie as she sat down on her aunt's bed. "But honestly, Aunt Marty, I don't remember it as being that bad. I used to enjoy it so much. Those singers and that comedian have really gone downhill since I last heard them."

"Tommie, I doubt that they've changed any at all," Aunt Marty remarked.

Tommie looked at her in astonishment. "Oh, but surely—"

"I believe you are the one who is different," Aunt Marty said. "Your standards have changed. You've been exposed to other and better influences, and the things you once enjoyed are distasteful to you now."

"Do you suppose that's it? I wasn't aware of any change," said Tommie.

"I think you've changed, Tommie, and I'm quite pleased about it," her aunt said.

"Anne didn't think we'd be allowed to go," Tommie remarked. "Did she think the program would be against Adventist standards?"

"I imagine so," replied Aunt Marty.

"Then why didn't she say so?" asked Tommie. "I still have much to learn about Adventist beliefs, and I appreciate having someone set me right on something I'm wrong about."

"Miss Croft and I discussed this venture at length," Aunt Marty said. "We had a fairly good idea as to what kind of program it was."

"Then why did you let us go?" Tommie demanded.

"We wanted you to find out for yourself how much you have changed, Tommie," Aunt Marty answered. "If we had told you the

95

program was no good, you wouldn't have believed it. You remembered it as being enjoyable, and you would have thought we were arbitrarily refusing you this innocent amusement. However, Miss Croft and I were both sure you would not stay and listen to that entire program, and our faith in you was justified!"

"I'm glad I didn't disappoint you," Tommie said thoughtfully. "I'm glad that I've changed so much. I wish all my rough edges could be smoothed off that painlessly."

"It would be nice, wouldn't it?" agreed Aunt Marty. "However, most things don't work out that way. You have to keep praying and striving. Run along to your room now. I'm going to blink the lights, and you'd better be in bed when they go out!"

When classes started the following week, Tommie's class, newly arrived at the status of juniors, found that their load would be lighter than it had been during the freshman year, but their responsibilities on the floors were correspondingly heavier.

Before long several of the girls were assigned to night duty, and among them was Anne. Tommie missed her roommate, especially during study period. They had been accustomed to discussing the lessons and comparing the notes taken in class.

One evening Tommie asked permission to study with Betty, whose roommate was also on night duty. Aunt Marty agreed, but cautioned the girls to be quiet. Betty's room was on the second floor, so Tommie tiptoed upstairs and into the room.

She and Betty studied and talked in low voices, but Tina heard them and slipped across the hall and into the room. She plopped herself down beside Betty, who was seated on the bed. Tina was in no mood to study that night. She wanted company and fun.

"Say, Tommie," she began, "aren't you getting a lot of letters from overseas lately?"

"A few," admitted Tommie. "They are from someone I've never met. But I do enjoy his letters."

"I've heard of these romances-by-mail," teased Tina.

"This is no such thing," Tommie answered indignantly. "One of the nice things about this correspondence is that we'll never meet, and therefore we can both write very frankly about ourselves and our feelings—even the things we don't tell those closest to us."

"Well, I'd be careful if I were you," retorted Tina. "This may get serious."

In the pause that followed these words, a step was heard on the stairs.

"That's Aunt Marty!" "That's Mrs. Perry!" whispered Tommie and Betty at the same moment.

Tina, instead of slipping back across the hall into her own room, threw herself headlong under Betty's bed. Her precipitous disappearance from view was so funny that both Tommie and Betty were having trouble controlling their laughter when Aunt Marty appeared in the doorway.

"Girls, girls! You're going to have to be more quiet!" Aunt Marty said sternly.

Tina had found a pencil under the bed and was vigorously poking through the thin mattress at Betty. Betty was having a hard time keeping a straight face, even though she and Tommie were being reprimanded.

At that moment Tommie glanced down to see Tina looking at her from under the bed. Tina immediately contorted her features into such a grotesque expression that Tommie had to giggle. She simply couldn't help it.

"Tommie, I think you had better go back to your own room and study alone," Aunt Marty said, and Tommie meekly obeyed.

"That rascal Tina," Tommie thought to herself. "I'll fix her. I'll short-sheet her bed tomorrow before she gets off duty. That is, if her roommate isn't in the room. Fran may be sleeping, since she's on night duty; if she is, I'll have to wait until they've gone to supper."

The next afternoon Tommie managed to carry out her plan. Shortly after lights out that night a head appeared around the edge of her door.

"S-s-s-st, Tommie!"

"Who is it?" Tommie asked.

"Tina!" came the reply. "I just wanted to tell you that I know a horrible punishment for people who short-sheet beds! So beware!"

Tommie smothered a giggle. "Why, what do you mean, Tina?" she asked in her most innocent voice.

Tina laughed softly. "As if you didn't know, you character! Well, don't say I didn't warn you!"

"Oh, boo, you don't scare me a bit," Tommie replied. "Good night, Tina. Go sleep under somebody's bed if you can't get between your own sheets!"

Tina giggled and crept away. Tommie smiled in the darkness, wondering what prank Tina had cooked up for her.

A few evenings later when study period was announced, Tommie stood inside her doorway, shaking her head in a puzzled way. "I've never before noticed how loud that clock ticks," she thought to herself. She picked up the clock, shook it, and replaced it in its accustomed spot on the dresser.

She stretched herself out on the bed to study. A moment later she frowned in bewilderment. "I'm going to have to have my ears checked," she muttered. "That clock sounds as if it were right under my head."

She looked under the bed. There was no clock there. A ghost of an idea glimmered in the back of her mind. She looked under the pillow. Still no clock. Then she lifted up the mattress. There it was!

"Ahh!" she thought delightedly. "So that's it. Tina really went to a lot of trouble for this one. Now let's see if I can find the rest of them."

Careful searching brought to light five more clocks that had been hidden in the room. Their alarms were set to go off at hourly intervals during the night.

Tommie placed the clocks in a row just outside the door and lettered a sign which she propped against them. "The owners of these clocks are invited to remove them at their earliest convenience."

Tina was the first one to pass by the door after study period was over. She stopped abruptly, read the sign, and then glanced up at Tommie, who was standing in the doorway openly laughing at her.

"Some of the girls have already taken their clocks, I see," she remarked casually as she picked her own clock out of the group.

"No," replied Tommie. "You're the first one. This is all there are!"

"Oh?" Tina lifted an inquiring eyebrow. "Are you sure?" Without waiting for an answer she went on back to her room.

"Oh, dear," thought Tommie. "Now, where can the rest of those clocks be hidden?" Lights would go out in twenty minutes, and she'd have to find them before then. All her frantic searching failed to turn up even one more clock. She looked unhappily at the disorder she had created in her search. "I'll have to spend all my off-duty time tomorrow straightening up this mess; and I still haven't found the rest of those clocks. They'll probably go off all night, and I won't get any sleep at all!"

Several times during the night Tommie awakened, but no ringing alarm pierced the silence of the room.

Early the next morning Tina stopped by and found Tommie irritably surveying the unkempt room.

"Did you find any more clocks, Tommie?" she asked.

"No," Tommie admitted.

"And you did all this looking for them?"

"Yes," Tommie replied.

Tina leaned against the wall and laughed heartily. "Tommie," she finally gasped, "you found all the clocks the first time. I just couldn't bear to find I'd gone to all that trouble for nothing, so I did the best I could to salvage something out of it. It looks as if I did all right!"

It tickled Tommie to see how she'd been tricked, and she joined Tina's laughter. "All right, Tina," she retorted. "You won this battle, but the war is not yet over. You just watch out!"

"I'll repeat your own words, Tommie: 'Oh, boo, you don't scare me one bit!'" And Tina turned away to her own room.

The next day Tommie made a quick trip downtown during her time off. She remembered seeing a most realistic toy snake in the window of the novelty shop, and she had thought of a good use for it. After making her purchase, she chuckled all the way home as she pictured the commotion that would ensue when Tina found the snake in her bed after lights-out.

To Tommie's chagrin, however, all was serene and quiet at bedtime. She wondered what had gone wrong with her prank, but soon she fell asleep.

Shortly after midnight the quiet of the dormitory was shattered by a series of unearthly shrieks. They came from Tina's room. The girls tumbled hastily out of bed and converged on the room. There was Fran, pale and shaking, clinging to Tina.

"I just got off night duty at midnight," she exclaimed, "and when I got into bed I felt something down at my feet and when I looked, there was that—that thing. Somebody take it away, please. I'm scared to death of snakes. Who would want to play a trick like that on me, anyhow?"

"Maybe whoever did it wasn't aware that you and I had changed beds recently," Tina observed with a laughing glance at Tommie.

"I'll take the snake, Fran," said Aunt Marty. "Now, you girls go back to bed. You've had enough excitement for one night!"

The next afternoon Tommie told Aunt Marty the whole story,

beginning with the night that Tina had hidden under Betty's bed.

Aunt Martly laughed heartily. "It sounds like some of the things that used to happen in our dormitory," she said. "I don't mind harmless pranks, but I think you and Tina had better call off your war. I think it's taking up too much of your time and energy."

"All right, Aunt Marty. We'll stop our playing. I'm more than willing. I always got the worst of it anyhow!" Tommie replied, and went off to find Tina to see what the surrender terms were.

Decision in a Snowstorm | 15

Tommie hurried from the sanitarium building to the first floor of the hospital. It was time to relieve the first-floor nurse for midnight supper.

"Well, here I am, Irene," she announced. "And you'd better make the most of it while I'm here. Tonight is my last time on night duty."

The other girl smiled. "And aren't you glad?"

"Well, it will be nice to be on days again. Sometimes I feel that I couldn't swear whether we have a sun in the sky or not, so little do I see of it," replied Tommie. "Now, is there anything I need to know about your patients while you're gone?"

"There's a baby in room 104 who had surgery today, and we are to try our hardest to keep him from crying. Such are the orders from Dr. Coulter! Other than that, there is nothing unusual," Irene said.

"You've locked the door?" Tommie asked, indicating the big front door of the hospital.

"Yep, at nine o'clock, as usual," Irene said. "I'll run along now. See you later!"

Tommie checked the baby and found him sleeping peacefully. Back at the nurses' station she sat down to watch for call lights. Then she heard voices outside the front door.

"Let's go in and raise a fuss," she heard a man say.

"Let's do," said another. Tommie was not worried, for Irene had said she'd locked the door. Tommie hoped the men would go quietly away when they found the door was locked, but if they made a commotion she could get the night supervisor, and she'd know what to do.

Suddenly the front door burst open and five young men staggered in. They were not much older than Tommie, but she was aware at once that they had been drinking. She started out of the nursing office, only to be sent spinning back when one of the group pushed her.

"No, you don't, nursie girl!" he panted. "You're going to stay ri'
here, see, and let us play football in your nice hospital." He stood in
the door and barred the way, but Tommie could see the other four
tossing a cap back and forth as they raced up and down the hall. The
phone on her desk was unconnected at night when the switchboard
operator went home, so there was no way to summon help. She
thought of calling out, but knew it would frighten the patients.
Then the baby in 104, awakened by the noise, began to cry!

"Please," Tommie pleaded with the young man barring the door,
"Please let me go see about the baby."

"Nothing doing, girlie! You're going to stay here!" He came close
and peered intently into her face. Tommie shrank back from his
alcoholic breath. "You've got freckles on your face, girl," he said owl-
ishly. "I didn't know they let freckled girls study to be nurses!"

In spite of her fear and worry about the baby, Tommie had to laugh
at such a ridiculous statement. At that moment Irene strode into the
hall, eyes flashing.

"You get out of here!" she blazed, and all five of the men took one
look at her angry face and marched meekly out.

Irene turned to Tommie. "You're going to get it, you just wait
and see! Letting those men in here, and flirting with them while that
baby in 104 cried! Just wait till I tell the night supervisor!"

"What do you mean, 'let those men in here'? You didn't lock that
door, and it was all your fault!" Tommie returned, her fear submerged
in anger. "And flirting? I was not doing any such thing; I was scared
to death of those drunks!"

"Then why didn't you get them out?" Irene demanded.

"Because I couldn't get out of the office, that's why. One of them
stood in the door!"

"They went when I told them to, didn't they?" said Irene. "If
you hadn't encouraged them to stay, they wouldn't have been here
when I got back."

"When I told them to leave, they just laughed at me," Tommie said.

"Sure they did; they knew you didn't mean it. Well, we'll see how
your nice little story holds up tomorrow when you tell it to Miss Croft!"

The session before the faculty the next day was painful. They took
the same attitude Irene did, and all Tommie's pleading seemed in
vain. Irene said she had locked the door; therefore, Tommie must
have opened it. Tommie didn't call for help; therefore, she appar-
ently didn't mind having the men there. Irene said Tommie was

laughing at one of them when she arrived; therefore she must have welcomed their attentions.

Tommie was sent to the dormitory and told to wait there for the faculty decision. It seemed a long two hours. At last she was called to the phone, and told their decision. She would be allowed to remain in training, but she was to understand that the faculty was deeply disappointed in her.

Tommie learned later that only Miss Barton and Elder McGee had prevented her dismissal from the school.

Now a week later, on day duty, she was more depressesd than she had been for a long time. She walked under a cloud, though she knew herself to be innocent of the charges.

Chapel was over, and in groups of two or three the girls were hurrying to get the morning report and go on duty. It was a morning to remember. Big snowflakes drifted lazily down and settled contentedly on the branches of the evergreens on the lawn and covered the ground with a fleecy blanket. They made a soft rustling sigh as they fell, aptly fitting the beauty of the scene.

Tommie lingered after the others had gone. She looked out over the lawn. The bright green of the cedars with the fluffy puffs of snow on the tips of the branches, the whispering flakes still falling, and the dark, graceful lines of the bare locust trees made an indelible impression on her mind.

"Oh, if I only had some time and if I had my paints here so I could get it on paper," she sighed longingly. Then her lips tightened determinedly, for in that moment she had made her decision. Soon she *would* have time; soon she would not be in the grip of the rigid routine that left no time for drawing or painting. In that brief moment she had decided to give up nursing! She had thought of it several times that week, but it seemed that if she quit she would be tacitly admitting the charges against her. But now—

She slipped her hand into the pocket of her jacket. Yes, the letter was still there. She had no need to take it out and read it again. Although it had come only the day before, she had read and reread until she knew it by heart.

"You know that I wanted you to illustrate children's books, and now has come the opportunity of a lifetime. I have recommended you for the job of illustrating a book written by a friend of mine, a book I believe will be very popular with children. I know you will make good; and when you do, there will be more important jobs open for you. Surely you will give up nursing for this? Anyone can be a nurse, but few have your artistic talent."

It was signed by Mrs. Hedges. In high school Mrs. Hedges had urged her to study art, and now she was offering her a specific opportunity to make something of her love of drawing and painting. Tommie nodded her head slightly. It was good someone believed in her. Yes, she would write a note of acceptance that very evening, as soon as she got off duty. She glanced at her watch and saw that she was already three minutes late.

"Oh, there you are, Miss Gordon," said the charge nurse. "We were about to start the report without you."

"I'm sorry I'm late," Tommie murmured as she slipped quietly into the group. She paid scant attention to what was said until the women's ward was mentioned. The eight patients there were her special charges, so she listened intently as that part of the report was given. The seventeen-year-old girl with rheumatic fever had suffered during the night; one of the late surgical patients had had her best night since surgery; the new patient admitted during the night was to go to surgery at eight-thirty, and so on. Even as she listened, however, the thought came to her mind that she would not stand in that room many more times to hear the morning report. It didn't make her as happy as she'd thought it would.

Then the night nurses were gone, and the day's work was before her. Tommie began to enumerate in her mind the duties that would take up the morning's time. There were the breakfast trays to be collected, the new patient's preoperative hypodermic to be given, the other bed to be made, baths, and little Jodie Brigham's treatment to be given as soon as possible. It would be a full morning.

She smiled as she thought of Jodie's treatment. Jodie, whose right knee and elbow were swollen and painful because of rheumatic fever, had laughingly named the offending members "Granny" and "Uncle Bob," and each morning she would report on how they had behaved during the time Tommie had been off duty. A braver and more cheerful girl would have been hard to find.

Student nurse Tommie stood silently in the door a moment before entering the ward. The girls who had given the morning cares had left it neat and clean, and the patients were chattering cheerfully to one another. It was a pretty sight—almost as pretty as the snowstorm outside, Tommie found herself thinking. One of the women glanced toward the door and saw her.

"There's Miss Gordon!"

Instantly there was a confused chorus. "Where have you been so long?" "There's our nurse!" "Look what a big breakfast I ate this morning, Miss Gordon!" And from Jodie in the corner, "My 'Granny' and 'Uncle Bob' sure cut a shine last night; but I knew that as soon as you put those hot things on them they'd calm down!"

The comments brought a glow to Tommie's heart, although she wasn't sure just why. Perhaps, she thought, it is because they believe in me and are glad to see me.

The new patient who was to have surgery that morning was apprehensive, and Tommie's first move was to reassure her. It was difficult at first, but after Tommie had offered a prayer, asking God to care for the patient and guide the surgeon's hands during the operation, the woman lay still, and even joked a bit when the girls from surgery came for her.

Jodie relaxed into a sound sleep after her treatment. Baths were given, and later dinner trays were distributed. The day passed, and at last it was time to give the evening cares. Backs were rubbed with alcohol, fresh water was provided, beds wrinkled by restless tossing were smoothed, and then it was time for Jodie's evening treatment.

Tommie made her way to the hydrotherapy room for fomentations.

During this slack period she had time to think, and try as she would to stifle them, certain questions kept raising themselves in her mind. As she turned on the steam in the fomentation tank and stood waiting for the packs to heat, words kept going around and around inside her head. "What makes you think God wants you to be an artist instead of a nurse—or have you even consulted Him about it?" "Do you think that book could give the happiness to others and to you that nursing will?" "How do you know that the book you propose to illustrate is one that a Seventh-day Adventist girl should read?" "Have you stopped to think that perhaps Satan is using these recent events to discourage you so you'll drop nursing? Are you going to play into the devil's hands that way?"

She turned off the steam with a snap and went back to the ward, her mind in real turmoil. Now she didn't know what to do. Oh, well, she would think it over later in the quietness of her room.

She gave the treatment quickly and gently. When it was done she queried smilingly, "Feeling better?"

Jodie's bright smile flashed in return. "Oh, yes, much better. Tell me, Miss Gordon, why do you do all this for us?"

Tommie replied mechanically, "Because I love my work and it gives me happiness to do it well!"

She had spoken from habit, but she suddenly realized the truth of the words. For the past week it had seemed she did not like nursing at all but that she didn't want to give it up because that would make her a quitter. Now, at the moment she was ready to leave, she had found out how much it meant to her.

Startled at her own thoughts, she repeated earnestly, "I do love my work, Jodie, and I want to spend my life helping others."

"I'm going to be a nurse, too, when I finish high school, Miss Gordon," smiled Jodie.

"I'm glad, Jodie. Nursing is a wonderful occupation," Tommie replied as she picked up the fomentations and started back to the hydrotherapy room.

She thought over her plans for the evening. "Well, one sure thing," she said to herself, "any note I write will be one of polite regret, saying I can't possibly accept the kind offer!"

Seven-thirty came, and it was time to go off duty. Tommie stood by each bed in turn and offered a short prayer for each patient. As she started out the door, she paused for one last look at the ward. There were eight serene faces; neat beds; and an atmosphere of content. "I'm glad I'm not giving this up," she said, shivering to think how close the decision had been.

That evening Tommie discussed her reversal of decision with Anne.

"Of course it started that night Irene forgot to lock the door," Tommie said. "I still can't understand why she insisted on making so much trouble for me over that episode. I would have reported it myself, but with her telling it her way first I didn't have a chance."

Anne thought a few minutes and then said, "The only reason I can think of is that as the senior nurse she was partly responsible for what you did. If her negligence had been proved she would have been dismissed from training. Of course it isn't fair for you to take the blame for the trouble she caused. On the other hand, Tommie, Irene may really believe the charges she made against you."

"I don't think she does, Anne," Tommie disagreed. "She hardly looks me in the face when I meet her in the hall now, and I wonder if she would have said anything different if I'd been dismissed from training."

"We may never know." After some moments of silence Anne

changed the subject. "Tommie, why don't you write up this story and send it to the *Youth's Instructor?* I think it would be of interest to any student nurse tempted to quit training!"

"Well-l-l, I guess I could try," Tommie said. "I've never done that type of writing; but to please you, I'll see what I can do. But you don't mean all of it, do you—I mean about Irene, and everything?" Tommie sounded alarmed. "I don't think that would be right."

"You're probably right," Anne admitted. "Just write about today, just as you told it to me."

"I'll try, but I won't promise how good it will be," Tommie replied.

Several days later the story was finished. Tommie called it "Decision in a Snowstorm." Anne read it and made a few suggestions. Tommie retyped it, sent it on its way, and then forgot about it.

A Senior Again | 16

Tommie shook her head unbelievingly. It was hard to realize she and her classmates were now seniors. This would be their last year in training.

She thought over the past two years. They had been particularly rewarding. She had gained self-confidence and poise along the way, and she recognized definite growth in her spiritual life.

As "Miss Teddy Bear" she was a frequent and welcome visitor to the orphanage. She and Anne were invited to the orphanage for special occasions, picnics, and holidays.

As "Miss Gordon" she knew she was developing into a capable nurse, one whose heart was in her work.

As "Tommie" she had changed too. When Mamma wrote that Jimmy Don was married, Tommie accepted the news without pain, hoping his marriage would be a happy one. Her own friendship with Chad Nolan had progressed so that she was writing him a letter every day, and he in turn wrote her every day. Of course, sometimes she would not receive any letters from him for several days, and then a group of three or four would arrive at once.

Tommie shook herself out of her reverie. That evening half the class would be leaving for affiliation at a hospital two hundred miles away. The group, including Anne, would take six months of specialized training in maternity and pediatric nursing. When the six months were over, the other half of the class would go.

After good-byes were said, a disconsolate group of seniors gathered in the parlor. The class had dwindled so that now only sixteen remained of the original twenty-three, and with half of the group gone, only eight seniors were left at the hospital. The unspoken thought in each heart that night was the knowledge that next year they'd all say good-bye again and go their separate ways.

The girls stood immersed in gloom as Miss Croft's secretary entered the dormitory and posted three notices on the bulletin board. Their troubles momentarily forgotten, the girls gathered around to read them.

One notice was the schedule of classwork for the seniors. Classes would begin in a few day and would be an even lighter load than the previous year. The second notice stated that because of the large number of girls coming in the new freshman class, four seniors were to move into the upstairs of the parsonage the next day. Tommie and Tina were on the list to move. The third notice was a change in work assignments. Tommie was to report at the diet kitchen at six the next morning.

The four girls who were to move to the parsonage went at once to inspect the rooms and to decide who would room with whom. Tina and Tommie chose a room with windows facing Miss Ruby's rock garden and then went to the dormitory to pack their belongings. They were instructed to put their boxes and suitcases in the hall outside their doors, and the hospital handyman was to move them to the parsonage the next day.

The next morning Tommie reported to the diet kitchen as ordered. She had been looking forward to serving there, for the dietitian, Mrs. Landis, a plump, motherly woman, was one of the most popular members of the hospital staff.

Shortly after breakfast Mrs. Landis reminded Tommie, "Don't forget to get weighed today!" The girls were weighed on the first day of every month, as a health check. Tommie's weight had remained the same after the first two months in training when she'd gained ten pounds. Now she remembered her only misgiving about working in the kitchen. She was afraid she'd gain weight. "I'll have to be extra careful," she reminded herself.

"One hundred twenty-one pounds, Miss Gordon," announced Miss Croft's secretary when Tommie stepped on the scales. "Last month—let's see—last month you weighed one hundred twenty-three. And you're five feet three inches tall. That's all right!"

Tommie hurried back to the kitchen to make salads for the dinner trays. They looked nice when she finished, but she was not hungry herself. When she had a few moments for her own meal, she drank a glass of buttermilk and ate a lettuce salad. It was so hot in the kitchen—and talking about food all day seemed to have ruined her appetite.

That afternoon Mrs. Landis told Tommie that it would be one of her jobs to visit each patient every day to find out any complaints about the meals or any preferences in the way of food. When Tommie had finished her rounds that first day, it was time to check the supper trays. Almost before she knew it the day was over.

As the days went by, Tommie decided she liked the diet kitchen best of all the places in the hospital. She thoroughly enjoyed preparing the food for the special diets, and in her talks with the patients she found many opportunities to point them to better dietary habits. Still, because of the unseasonably hot weather and her constant work with food, she ate very little. Only buttermilk and lettuce appealed to her.

Time went by so fast that it came as a surprise when Mrs. Landis reminded her one morning, "It's time to be weighed again, Miss Gordon!"

Tommie smiled. "It doesn't seem possible I've been in the diet kitchen a month. I've enjoyed it, and I'm glad I have another month left on this service."

"I'll be gone the last two weeks of this month," Mrs. Landis said. "Then you'll be in full charge. Do you mind?"

"Not at all," replied Tommie. She had no doubt about her ability to handle the kitchen for two weeks.

"I think you'll do a fine job," said Mrs. Landis. "Now, don't forget to get weighed."

Tommie went along to the nursing office and stepped on the scales. Miss Croft's secretary looked at her records.

"You weighed one hundred twenty-one pounds last month," she observed. "Let's see how you did during your month in the kitchen. Most girls gain a little during their two months there."

"I think I lost a little," Tommie said. "My uniforms seem loose."

Miss Hope looked down at the dial on the scales. "Step off a minute, will you, Miss Gordon? Someone has been tampering with these scales. I'll have to adjust them."

Tommie obediently stepped aside and the other woman stooped and put her hand on the adjusting knob, but she didn't move it.

"That's odd," she murmured. "Everything seems all right. Here, Miss Gordon, let's try it again."

Back on the scales again, Tommie glanced at the dial for herself. One hundred seven pounds. Why, that was surely impossible! That was a loss of—hmmmmm—fourteen pounds—and all in one month!

"Wait here a moment, Miss Gordon," Miss Hope said. "I want to talk to Miss Croft about this."

Several minutes later Tommie was ushered into Miss Croft's office. "Why, what does this mean, my dear child?" Miss Croft questioned her. "Haven't you been feeling well?"

"I've felt fine," Tommie answered truthfully. "I just haven't been hungry."

"Evidently you haven't, since you've lost fourteen pounds," said Miss Croft. "Have you been eating anything at all?"

"Oh, yes! I've been eating lettuce—and buttermilk—" Tommie began, and then stopped.

"Yes. Go on," Miss Croft encouraged her. "What else have you been eating?"

"Just lettuce and buttermilk, I guess," said Tommie. "Nothing else tastes good. It has been so hot in the kitchen."

"My dear child, you are going to have to eat or we'll have to transfer you out of the kitchen until the weather is cooler. I'll tell you what you do. When it's time for your meals, take your food out under those trees back of the sanitarium building. Relax there in the shade for a bit until you are cooler, and then try to eat. I want you to come back and be weighed a week from today, and if you've lost even one ounce, we'll have to take you out of the kitchen!"

Tommie agreed to try it, and she found it was easier to eat in the shade of the trees, although she still wasn't hungry. At the end of the week she had gained half a pound, so she was allowed to stay on in the kitchen.

That month, too, went fast, and almost before Tommie knew it, she was posted for her two months in surgery. She had heard enough about surgery to fill her with fear and trembling. All her other classmates had, two by two, had their surgical training, but the girl who was to have been Tommie's partner had dropped out of training, so now Tommie's name was posted with Elaine Webb, one of the junior nurses.

At first the two girls only washed the surgical linen, and then the instruments. Soon the day came when they were allowed to be circulating nurses, filling pans of solutions and counting sponges. Along with these duties they were learning which instruments were used for different kinds of surgeries. They were also on call for deliveries, and not many nights passed before they learned to jump out of bed at the first ring of the phone. Some nights when a delivery seemed imminent they didn't go to their rooms at all but slept at the hospital until they were needed.

During this time Tommie and Elaine were becoming fast friends. In the wee hours of morning, cleaning up surgery after a delivery or emergency appendectomy, or early in the day as they set up for a major operation, they kept up a steady stream of talk, except when the doctors or supervisors were near.

One day the surgery schedule was unusually light—only one minor surgery.

"You girls can use this extra time to sterilize some supplies," the surgery supervisor said. "We need several flasks of green soap done. You'll find a list in the workroom. Then while those things are in the sterilizer, you can count and package sponges, since we're low on those too."

"I'll pack these things in the sterilizer," Elaine said when the supplies were assembled, "if you'll go up to the storeroom to get the sponges."

"All right; I'll get the key from the lab," replied Tommie and went on her way.

The girls were busily counting sponges when the supervisor came back from dinner. "Are those things in the sterilizer ready to come out yet?" she asked.

Tommie looked at the clock. "In about six or seven minutes," she answered.

"All right. Don't forget them. I'm going across the hall where it's quiet so I can do the paper work on this surgery."

When the bell rang indicating that it was time to open the sterilizer, Elaine said, "I'll go ahead and open the sterilizer, Tommie."

"All right," said Tommie. "I'll be there as soon as I finish counting this bunch of sponges."

When Tommie entered the workroom, Elaine was opening the door of the big sterilizer, and as she did so a flask of still-boiling liquid soap fell from the sterilizer to the floor and shattered. The boiling liquid splashed over Elaine's foot as the flask broke.

In less than a breath Tommie was at Elaine's side, stripping off the soaked shoes and hose. The supervisor had heard the noise and hurried in. She immediately took Elaine downstairs to the doctor's office, and Tommie mopped up the spilled soap and finished putting surgery to rights.

The supervisor came back just as it was time for Tommie to go to class. "You may go, Miss Gordon. Miss Webb has been put to bed in the sanitarium. Her burns aren't as bad as we'd feared."

Tommie hurried into the classroom ahead of Miss Barton. When all had taken their places, Miss Barton said, "Before we begin our regular class session I have an announcement to make. Because of the quick action on the part of one of the senior nurses a member of the junior class has been spared a serious injury." She then went on to tell about the accident in surgery, ending with, "Miss Webb says that when the hot soap splashed on her, she jumped, and almost before her feet touched the floor again Miss Gordon had gotten her shoes and hose off. What did you think, Miss Gordon, when you saw the accident?"

Tommie felt ashamed. She hated to admit that she hadn't thought, but in all honesty she was compelled to do so. "I didn't think at all," she confessed. "I just saw what happened, and before I even realized it myself I acted."

"I'm very proud of the way you reacted in an emergency, Miss Gordon," said Miss Barton with an approving smile. "If you hadn't acted as you did, if you'd stopped to think, Miss Webb would have suffered serious burns. As it is, they are not too bad. She has you to thank for that."

Tommie was sure any other member of the class would have done the same, but she welcomed her teacher's praise.

Elaine was back to work in a few days, and there was a closer bond than ever between the two girls.

Shortly after the middle of November Tommie decided to have her picture taken so she might give copies as Christmas gifts. She had let her hair grow since the first week she was in training, and now it was quite long. The hospital rule that each student nurse wear her hair in one roll around her head both on duty and off left little scope for individuality in hair style. Tommie felt that the prescribed hair style was unflattering to her, and she certainly didn't want it that way when her picture was taken.

When she mentioned her problem to the operating supervisor she said, "I'll tell you what, Miss Gordon. Put your hair up in pin curls tonight and then wear a surgical cap over them when you come to work in the morning. When you have off-duty time tomorrow afternoon, comb out your hair just before you leave for town but put it down inside your coat collar. After your picture is taken put your hair up again in a roll and come on back to the hospital."

It sounded feasible, so Tommie did as the supervisor advised. When she combed her hair into place in the photographer's studio, she

113

felt very proud of the curls and waves. It had been a long time since she'd seen her hair that way.

After the picture was taken she couldn't bring herself to put her hair up in one roll again but left it hanging down her back as she walked home. After several blocks, however, she became uneasy and finally put her hair down inside her coat and pulled the collar up. A few minutes later a car drew up beside her and stopped.

"Miss Gordon, let me give you a lift back to the dormitory!" It was Doctor Coulter, owner of the hospital and nursing school.

Tommie got in the car, but she never had a ride she enjoyed less. She was breaking one of the rules, and she was afraid she'd been caught at it. If Dr. Coulter had seen her wearing the forbidden hair style, he never mentioned it then or afterward.

The pictures were finished the next week, and Tommie mailed them right away. Chad Nolan was in Japan now, and he had specifically asked for a picture of her. She hoped he would receive it in time to consider it a Christmas gift.

Not long after Christmas vacation was over Tommie received a letter from Chad saying that he had received the picture and was very happy to have it. His big news was that he was being discharged from the Army and was going home. He wrote that he wanted her to continue writing to him and gave her his home address. Tommie saw that he lived in the town where one of the larger Adventist colleges was located—the college where her aunts had gone and where she herself was planning to take her premed training. "We may meet sometime, after all," she thought. She hoped they would.

Tommie continued writing daily, and ten days later she again heard from Chad. He was home in time to start the second semester at the college, to go ahead with his premed course.

Tommie wrote him that the next day she would be leaving for affiliation, and gave him her new address. She then packed her suitcase and joined the other seven seniors in the parlor to discuss plans for the coming trip.

Tommie, Rita, Elise, and Betty were assigned to the maternity wing in the large general hospital, and the other four girls, Wendy, Nellie, Jean, and Tina, went to the children's hospital on the other side of the city. Since the girls had every Sabbath off, they planned to get together and spend Sabbath afternoons first at one dormitory and then at the other. They made their plans, but they reckoned without the members of the local Adventist church.

The first Friday afternoon Wendy phoned and announced, "Girls, I've accepted a dinner invitation for all of us tomorrow. You'll know the lady when you see her. She's Mrs. Jasper. She had surgery at our hospital last year!"

Mrs. Jasper! Why, of course Tommie remembered. Inoperable cancer had been the diagnosis, but Dr. Coulter had decided to use radium anyhow. As he had expressed it, "The whole church is praying for her, and I'll do my part by using radium." Five days later when the radium had been removed, there was no sign of malignancy. Yes, Tommie remembered. It had been a miracle of healing.

The girls were warmly welcomed at church the next day. Miss Croft's brother-in-law was pastor of the church, and he was happy to have the student nurses in his congregation. After the service the girls were deluged with invitations for dinner, but Mrs. Jasper smilingly warded off the others, saying, "The girls are mine for today. You'll just have to wait your turn!"

Mr. Jasper's mode of transportation was a panel truck which he used in his dry-cleaning business. There was plenty of room for the eight nurses and the three Jasper children.

When they reached the Jasper home, Mr. Jasper made an announcement. "Now, girls, you've been invited here to dinner, but there were strings attached to that invitation. You see, when your classmates were here, they always called us Mom and Dad and made themselves right at home. If they were hungry, they raided the refrigerator; if they were sleepy, they took a nap; if they had problems, they came to us. Unless you promise to do the same, I'm afraid you won't get any dinner!"

Of course the girls promised, and the dinner was delightful. When it was over, everyone got into the truck again and they were taken for a ride through the lovely historical city and the surrounding countryside.

It was the first of many such rides in the panel truck. Whenever business took the Jaspers into the country, they first called the dormitories to see who of the girls were off duty and wanted to go along.

One day in the middle of the first week Tommie stopped at the mailbox outside the cafeteria to wait for her classmates. There was a letter from Chad, and she read it as she waited.

"From that smile, I'd say that was a pretty good letter!"

Tommie looked up to see who had spoken. A young couple stood there, smiling at her.

"We are Don and Bonnie Carelli," explained the young woman. "We saw you in church last Sabbath, but we didn't get a chance to speak to any of you."

"I'm Tommie Gordon," Tommie introduced herself.

"Oh, you're Anne's roommate," exclaimed Don Carelli. "She told us about you. She used to read your letters to us when she was here." Tommie blushed as she recalled some of the nonsense she had written to Anne.

"I work in Central Supply, and Don is one of the laboratory technicians," Bonnie said. "If you ever need any help or run into anything you don't understand here at the hospital, just come to us."

The other girls arrived about that time and were introduced.

"Are you girls off duty at three this afternoon?" asked Don. "If you are, why don't you meet us here and go home with us for supper?" He turned to his wife. "We can feed a crowd this size, can't we?"

"Of course," Bonnie replied.

Thus it was that the girls spent the first of many happy evenings at the Carelli apartment.

Within a few weeks the girls were taking an active part in church work. Tommie and Elise taught in the primary division of the Sabbath School; all except Wendy and Rita sang in the choir, and they all took turns helping Don Carelli with the Pathfinders.

One day about the middle of April, Betty asked her roommates, "Do

116

any of you have any money? I'm without one cent, and I want to run out to Mom and Dad Jasper's. Could one of you lend me bus fare?"

"I don't have any money," Elise answered. "I won't have any for another week or so. I'm sorry, Betty."

"Me, either," Tommie observed sadly. "I lost the five dollar bill Aunt Nola sent me the first of the month, and I'll be without any until the first of next month."

"I have three pennies," said Rita. "Aren't we a poverty-stricken lot, though?"

"I guess we'll just have to do those things that don't cost anything," said Elise.

"I don't mind," said Tommie. "I'll stay home and write letters."

The next afternoon Tommie's dresser drawer stuck. She gave it a vigorous tug, and it came all the way out. When she started to replace it, she noticed an envelope that had slipped down behind the drawer. Closer inspection showed it to be the one Aunt Nola had sent the first of the month. And the five dollar bill was still in it!

Tommie drew a deep breath. "Well, we aren't rich, but we're five dollars short of being broke!"

The next day she received a letter from Aunt Josie, and a check for $25. Aunt Josie said that she, too, would send Tommie a small amount of money each month until she graduated. It was wonderful to have the extra money. Tommie put it away for emergency use and shared with the other girls the five dollars she'd recovered.

In May Tommie and her group were transferred to the children's hospital, and the other four girls went to the general hospital. Now they all began to think seriously about the State Board examinations which would be coming the third week in August. Don Carelli had lent them his State Board review book, and the girls studied from it each day.

Tommie loved the work at the children's hospital. Anne had paved the way for her by telling the patients that Miss Gordon would draw pictures for them when she came. Some of the patients had been in the hospital for months and would be there months longer.

Libby, a lively six-year-old, was in the hospital for the correction of a clubfoot. Whenever she was naughty, she would be put in the bathroom in the empty bathtub, away from the other children in the ward. One day when she had been far naughtier than usual, Tommie picked her up and started for the bathtub. Libby rebelled. She

117

snatched Tommie's cap and threw it on the floor; she grabbed Tommie's black tie and twisted it back over her shoulder; then she began to unbutton the front of Tommie's uniform, all the while screaming at the top of her lungs. She had managed to unfasten the top two buttons when the nurse in charge arrived to rescue Tommie. Together they put Libby in the bathtub, and Tommie repaired herself and her uniform as best she could and continued her work, still chagrined at being bested by a six-year-old.

The second week in August Tommie came to dinner one day, her eyes dancing, her cheeks bright with color. Strangely enough, she wasn't hungry.

"Tommie, are you ill?" queried Elise.

"No, not at all," Tommie smiled. "I'm just happy. You see, Aunt Nola just sent me $60 to help with my graduation expenses."

"I've a feeling you aren't telling us all the story," Rita said shrewdly.

"Well, yes, there is more," admitted Tommie. "The big news is, next week I'm going to have a visitor!"

"Who?" The word came as one from the other three.

"Chad Nolan!" Tommie sat back, delighted at the sensation this information created. "He'll be here for five days during the time we're taking State Boards!"

"Tommie, you'll fail those tests, for sure!" Rita declared.

"I will not," Tommie contradicted. "I've studied hard, and when the time comes, visitor or no visitor, I'll know what to put down."

"You'd better eat," advised Elise. "You'll be sick if you don't. I remember that once—when you were in the kitchen, remember?—you went a month with practically nothing to eat and lost fourteen pounds without getting sick, but you might not be so lucky this time!"

"I'm too excited to eat right now, Elise. I just got Chad's letter a few minutes ago. And just think! I still have the money Aunt Josie sent me, so I can get my hair cut, a permanent, and a couple of new dresses!"

"Someone put a brick on Tommie's head! She's flying too high," teased Rita.

"I'll calm down. But isn't it exciting? After writing to each other for over two years we're actually going to meet. It's going to be a long week, though!"

"When will he get here?" Elise asked.

"Sabbath morning. We have State Board tests Tuesday and

Wednesday, and he's going back Wednesday night. We'll be going back to the home hospital Thursday morning. He's coming at a busy time, but I'm so glad he's coming."

During the rest of the week Tommie had her hair cut and set, shopped for new dresses, and told practically everyone she knew that Chad was coming.

"Oh, please have Sabbath dinner with us," begged Bonnie Carelli.

"We want to take you and your young man for a ride with the rest of us on Sabbath afternoon," said Dad Jasper.

Tommie went to the head nurse on Friday to ask for a Saturday night late leave. The students were allowed one late leave a week. They were allowed to stay out until midnight. Other nights they had to be in at ten-thirty. Tommie had never asked for a late leave before.

"You say you are going to have a friend visiting here, Miss Gordon?" asked the head nurse when Tommie made her request.

"Yes, ma'am. He'll be here for five days."

"He will be leaving Tuesday or Wednesday, then?"

"On Wednesday," replied Tommie. "On the train that leaves here at one o'clock in the morning. It will be Thursday morning, actually."

"All right. Here's your late leave," smiled the head nurse. "Do be careful not to lose it!"

"Thank you so much," said Tommie. As she went back to the dormitory, she glanced at the slip of paper and stopped short! The paper stated that student nurse Tommie Gordon had late leave until midnight on Saturday, Sunday, Monday, and Tuesday nights, and until 1:30 a.m. on Wednesday night!

"Isn't that thoughtful of her," Tommie said to herself. "I guess it's because I have never asked for a late leave before."

Chad had written that he'd see her at the dormitory on Sabbath morning. The other girls tactfully went to Sabbath School early, and Tommie waited and watched out the upstairs window.

She watched the taxi drive up and the young man get out. "He's much nicer looking than his pictures," she thought as she fairly flew down the stairs.

There was no shyness between them as there would have been had they been meeting for the first time under ordinary circumstances. They had written each other their hopes and dreams and inmost feelings for over two years, and now they just took up in

119

person where the letters had left off, and they talked happily all the way to church.

After church Chad was introduced to the other girls, and then he and Tommie were whisked off by the Carellis.

"Mr. Jasper is coming over at two o'clock to take us all for a drive," Don Carelli said after dinner.

"He may be a little later than that if he stops to pick up the other girls first," observed Tommie.

However, Dad Jasper was prompt, and when the Carellis and Chad and Tommie got into the truck, the other girls were already there.

"Tommie, you and Chad are special guests today," said Dad Jasper. "Where do you want to go?"

"Chad has never been here before," replied Tommie. "Why don't you take us around like you did the first Sabbath we were here? After all, this is our last Sabbath here too."

"That's what we'll do." And away they went.

"I brought along the latest *Youth's Instructor,*" said Bonnie. "I'll see if there is something we can read as we go." A few moments later she exclaimed, "Tommie! Did you write this story in the *Instructor?*"

"No," answered Tommie without looking.

"But it has your name by it," Bonnie insisted. "It's called "Decision in a Snowstorm.' "

Then Tommie remembered. That was the story she'd written and sent to the *Instructor* over a year before. She'd forgotten it.

"Oh—oh, yes—I guess I did write that," she acknowledged. "The editor wrote that she'd received it but she didn't say whether or not they could use it, so I forgot about it. May I see it?"

The magazine passed from hand to hand as everyone had to see the story with Tommie's name on it. Then Bonnie read it aloud.

"That's wonderful," Chad commented.

"Shakespeare himself never did better," teased Dad Jasper.

"I'll get you to help me with English when you come to college," smiled Chad.

"Are you going to continue writing?" asked Don Carelli.

Tommie looked surprised. "No," she answered. "That story was —well, it was sort of an accident. It was an incident I felt quite strongly about, and I wrote it as I felt it. It isn't likely that I'll find anything else I feel strongly enough about to write."

The afternoon passed pleasantly. At sundown the group had worship high on a mountaintop overlooking the town.

"Dad, would you stop at the hospital so we can see if we have any mail?" asked Wendy.

"Be glad to," Dad Jasper replied.

"Tommie won't have any. Her correspondent is right here," teased Tina.

Wendy got back into the car waving a handful of envelopes. "Our grades came," she explained, handing out the letters.

Tommie looked at her grades proudly. As they passed their grade slips around and compared them, it was plain that Tommie's were the best in the class. Then as she replaced her grades in the envelope, she found a note she hadn't noticed before.

"Dear Miss Gordon,

You have a fine record here, but I am disappointed in you. If you had done your best, I would have had to revise my grading system.

Sincerely,
J. Barton, R.N."

Tommie realized sadly that what Miss Barton had written was true—she hadn't done her best. She was no longer proud of her grades.

That night when Tommie got in from her late date she found her roommates still awake. She heard them laughing and talking as she came into the room. "What's the joke?" she asked.

"We were just saying that if you had deliberately arranged things so you could make a good impression on Chad, you couldn't have done better than the way things just happened," said Rita. "That story, and your good grades, I mean."

"That is what I call the nicest kind of coincidence," Tommie grinned. "Still, I think Chad had already formed his impressions of me before he got here, just as I formed mine of him. I'll not deny, though, that those things today helped." She yawned. "I'm going to bed. I have another late leave tomorrow night, so I'd better sleep while I have a chance."

Graduation | 18

Early next morning Tommie's roommates were eager to hear Tommie's impressions of her friend.

"He seems awfully nice," observed Elise.

"Is he the kind of person you thought he'd be?" asked Betty.

"Yes, he is," replied Tommie. "After all, we did get well acquainted through letters during the past two years."

"I take it you like him," teased Rita.

"Yes, I do. I'm going to marry him!" Tommie said calmly.

"You mean he's already asked you? And you've accepted?" gasped Elise.

"No, of course not. He doesn't even know about it. But you just wait and see. I'm going to marry him someday," Tommie replied.

"She'll do it, too," Betty declared. "That poor young fellow doesn't have a chance. Do you think we ought to warn him?"

"Don't you dare!" commanded Tommie. "When the time comes, I want him to think it is all his idea!"

That day and the next Tommie and Chad spent their time leisurely seeing the city and hiking in the mountains. On Monday afternoon they sat in front of the hospital waiting for a bus. Tommie mentioned that State Board examinations would start the next day.

"I've studied hard so I'm not really worried about them," she said.

"What subjects do you have tests in?" Chad asked.

"Anatomy and physiology, nursing arts, chemistry, surgical arts, dietetics, pediatrics, obstetrics, and psychology. There are probably others, but those are the ones I can think of right now!"

"I got out of the Army in time to take the last semester of college this year, and one course I took was chemistry," Chad said. "I remember one experiment we did showing how the accumulation of lactic acid in muscles causes fatigue." He went on to describe the experiment and its results.

122

The next morning the students filed into the large auditorium to take their places. Senior students from various sections of the state were there. After the papers were passed out, the room was quiet. At noon Tommie and her classmates discussed the tests they'd taken. They were relieved to find the tests hadn't been as hard as they'd feared.

"I didn't know the technical names for many of the binders we use," said Tommie. "Did we learn them?"

"Yes, during our freshman year," said Wendy, "but afterward we used the common names for them."

"Well, that was a seven-point question, and I doubt if I got more than two points on it," sighed Tommie.

"You passed, didn't you?" teased Betty.

"I know I passed," answered Tommie. "I wanted to do better than pass." She was still unhappy over the note that had come with her grades.

That afternoon the chemistry test was given. Tommie was surprised to find two questions dealing with the relationship of lactic acid to fatigue. She was able to answer them, recalling the experiment Chad had told her about.

As soon as the tests were over, Wendy exclaimed, "Say, wasn't that chemistry test hard? Did any of you get those questions on lactic acid?"

"I did," Tommie answered.

"But I don't remember ever studying that," said Tina.

"I don't, either," said Wendy. "When did we study that, Tommie?"

"I don't remember whether or not we studied that in class, but Chad explained all about it to me yesterday," Tommie said smugly.

"Well, talk about luck!" exclaimed Wendy. "Do you think he'd review us on some of the subjects we're having tests on tomorrow?"

"He'd likely be willing, if he knew anything about them. You expect a premed student to know about chemistry, but how much would he know about pediatrics or dietetics?" was Tommie's reply.

"Or surgical nursing?" chimed in Betty.

"He may know more about surgery than you think," smiled Tommie. "He was a surgical technician in the Army, remember, and he's scrubbed for lots of surgeries. Anyway, I'm not going to study tonight. I'd only get mixed up. Dad Jasper has asked us all to come out there for the evening. Chad's already out there, and Dad Jasper will be here any minute to pick us up. Do you want to go, or stay and review?" She looked questioningly at her classmates.

"I'll go," decided Rita. "I'm like you, Tommie. There's no use for me to cram now—I'd get more confused. An evening of fun will benefit me, I think."

"Same here," agreed most of the others.

"I'm going to stay here and go to bed early," smiled Elise. "I need a good night's sleep before those tests tomorrow."

"We'll come home early," promised Wendy. "All of us except Tommie, that is. She doesn't need sleep!"

Tommie laughed. "It's food I can get along without, not sleep. I'll probably come home early too, since I have a late leave until 1:30 tomorrow night."

At three o'clock Wednesday afternoon the tests were over. The girls were jubilant—the ordeal of State Board had been hanging over them for months. Dad Jasper took everyone out to dinner to celebrate. It was a gay occasion.

At ten o'clock the other girls went back to the dormitory to pack, as they were leaving early the next morning.

"We'll pack your things, Tommie," offered Elise, "since you'll be late getting in."

"Oh, will you, Elise?" Tommie said gratefully. "I'd appreciate it so much."

"What are you and Chad going to do until his train leaves?" asked Wendy.

"Just talk, I guess," answered Tommie.

"But that's all you've done this past five days," laughed Wendy.

"Did you ever know me to run out of words?" asked Tommie.

"Now that I think of it, I don't believe I ever did," replied Wendy. "But Chad doesn't have much to say to the rest of us. He is polite, but he does most of his talking to you."

"Of course he does most of his talking to me," Tommie said. "I'm the one he came here to see. Besides, he's a little shy."

"I suppose Dad Jasper will take you to the depot when it's time?" queried Tina.

"Yes," answered Tommie. "And then he'll bring me back to the dorm. Don't wait up for me," she added with a grin.

"We won't," said Wendy. "You'll probably sleep all the way back on the train tomorrow, though!"

The eight girls settled themselves comfortably in one end of the day coach for the ride back to the home hospital.

"Let's make graduation plans," suggested Wendy as soon as the train pulled out of the station and they could no longer see the Jasper family waving good-bye.

"Hadn't we better wait until we're all together?" asked Betty. "Some of the other girls may have ideas too."

"We can make plans now," answered Wendy, "and when we get together we can pool them and select which ones we want."

"That sounds reasonable," approved Elise.

"We need an aim and a motto," said Rita. "Does anyone have any suggestions?"

All were silent for several minutes. Then Tommie spoke up rather diffidently. "I selected a personal motto and aim when I came into training. I'll give them to you to get things started."

"All right, Tommie," said Wendy. "I'll write them down, and then the rest of you girls give us some ideas."

"My motto is 'Not to be ministered unto, but to minister,' and my aim is 'To be like Him.' "

Again the girls were silent. Then Wendy said thoughtfully, "I doubt if we'd ever find another motto and aim better suited to a class of student nurses!"

"We don't need more suggestions," Elise said decisively. "I like Tommie's motto and aim, and unless the other girls come up with better ones, I think we should use these."

"Good!" approved Wendy. "Now I have a suggestion. As far as I know, the seniors have never had a class night. Why don't we be the first to have one?"

"What would that involve?" asked Jean.

"Well, I thought we might each pay special tribute to someone who has helped us during training—parents if they are here, and if they aren't, then perhaps someone on the hospital staff," said Wendy.

"We could have a class history," said Tina.

"And a class prophecy, maybe," added Tommie.

"I know a good way to give the class prophecy," spoke up Rita. "We've already planned to keep a round robin letter going. Let's have someone read a letter supposedly written ten years from now!"

"That's a grand idea," applauded Wendy.

"Graduation is only ten days away," mused Elise. "It doesn't seem possible we've been in training three years."

"It certainly doesn't," agreed Tommie. "When I was a freshman, these three years seemed to stretch ahead of me forever; now it seems as if they went by in three weeks."

"I'll be glad to get back and see my roommate," said Rita.

"So will I," said Tommie. "Anne wrote in her last letter that she had some special news for me, and I can hardly wait to hear what it is."

"It's going to be a busy time," said Tina. "We'll be practicing for graduation and working on the floors."

"But it will be good to be back," said Wendy. "Even if it is only for two weeks."

An excited and happy group of senior nurses were reunited that afternoon. Anne hurried Tommie into their room as soon as they could get away from the group.

"Tommie, guess what! I have a job waiting for me as soon as we graduate. I found out today. I'm going to work in a doctor's office in Colorado!"

"Wonderful, roommate," responded Tommie. "I've filled out my application for college, and I'm sure I can get a job near there in one of the hospitals. My cousin Val is going to college there, and he's been inquiring around. He says the hospitals are short of nurses. There's a state hospital for crippled children, and I'm going to apply there first. That's the type of nursing I like best." She paused. "But wait a minute, Anne. Your new job can't be the news you were waiting to tell me, because you said you only found out about the job today. What else do you have to tell me?"

"I finally broke my engagement to Ben!" Anne announced.

"Oh, Anne!" Tommie murmured sympathetically. "Was it hard?"

"No, not really," replied Anne. "He's been gone so long, and our letters were getting farther and farther apart. I think it was a big relief to both of us."

"That's good," said Tommie with a sigh of relief. "I'm glad it was easy for you."

"You wrote me that Chad was coming to see you, and then you never wrote another word," reminded Anne.

"I was busy," laughed Tommie. "I'll tell you about it right now, though."

Later, as Tommie was finishing her story, Elaine Webb came rushing in. "I'm so glad to see you, Tommie," she cried. "You're to work on second floor tomorrow, the same as I am, and there's a patient in the maternity ward who sent a special message to you. She wants you to come and see her as soon as you go on duty."

"Who is she?" asked Tommie.

"I'm not supposed to tell," returned Elaine.

"Then I'll have to curb my curiosity until morning," said Tommie.

"Suppertime, girls," said Wendy passing the door. "Then a class meeting afterward."

The next morning when Tommie went on duty, the night nurse said, "Miss Gordon, Mrs. Martin in the maternity ward wants to see you after the report is given."

"I don't remember a Mrs. Martin," said Tommie thoughtfully. "Although I must have been here when she had a baby before."

"No, this is her first baby," said Elaine, leaving Tommie more puzzled than ever.

The name was unfamiliar, but the face was not, Tommie found as she entered the ward. "Why, Ginny Cobb! Ginny Martin, I mean!" she exclaimed.

"Hello, Miss Gordon," smiled Ginny. "I was hoping you'd get back from affiliation before I left the hospital."

"And you have a baby, Ginny! Tell me about it? Is it a boy or a girl?"

"A boy," Ginny said proudly. "He weighed almost eight pounds— seven pounds and fifteen ounces, to be exact. He's the biggest baby in the nursery, and he yells the loudest when he gets hungry!"

Tommie laughed. "I'll go see him the minute I leave this room," she promised.

"Isn't it odd," Ginny said reflectively, "that we met the day you came to take training, and now three years later you're ready to graduate and get your R.N., and I'm married and have a baby?"

"Lots of things happen in three years, and we change in many ways," smiled Tommie. "I don't imagine either of us would wish things to be any different."

"You're right," agreed Ginny.

"Anne, is my cap on straight?" Tommie asked for the fifth time.

"Yes, it is," replied Anne. "Do I look all right?"

"You look fine," Tommie assured her. "Are you jittery?"

"A little," Anne admitted.

"I have butterflies as big as eagles in my stomach," announced Tommie.

127

Anne giggled. "Chin up, roommate. It's only graduation!"

" 'Only graduation,' she says," groaned Tommie. "Only the day we've been planning and working toward for three years!"

"And practicing for, for ten days," reminded Anne. "What could possibly go wrong?"

"I don't know, only I'm nervous," said Tommie.

"Let's go into the parlor and see how the other girls look," suggested Anne. "We're both ready, so come on."

The seniors surveyed each other, proud in their crisp white uniforms and black-striped caps.

"You know what?" demanded Lucille. "When I get married, I'm going to have the organist play 'Pomp and Circumstances' instead of the wedding march. I've marched to 'Pomp and Circumstances' all my life and I'm too old to change to something else!"

"Time to go to the church, girls," announced Wendy.

The walk to the church took a couple of minutes and, as the girls got into their marching positions outside the rear door, Tommie could look in and see the aim and motto she had chosen, written above the pulpit in lovely red and gold lettering. "Not to be ministered unto, but to minister." "To be like Him."

She breathed a silent prayer that those words would remain always a part of her life and her dedication to nursing.

The girls marched in, and the service proceeded. Almost before they were aware of it, it was time for the presentation of the diplomas. As her name was called, each girl crossed the platform to receive the precious document.

"Tommie Elizabeth Gordon!"

As Tommie walked across the platform, she thought, "Once, years ago, I promised myself that one day I'd march across here and receive my diploma. This is one dream that came true!"

Tommie's eyes sparkled, and it was with difficulty that she kept from laughing aloud, which of course would never do in a crowded depot. But it was such a good joke—Elise and Tina arriving on the same train, and neither knew the other was coming.

A few minutes later she spotted the two girls coming up the ramp together. She hurried to them. There was a happy babble of voices as they met. After some minutes of animated talk, Elise and Tina collected their luggage and Tommie hailed a taxi.

As they were driven toward the hospital, Elise said, "I saw Tina sitting ahead of me in the coach, and I could hardly believe my eyes!"

"When someone touched my shoulder and I looked up to see Elise there, I was so surprised I couldn't say a word," Tina added. "It was really grand to find out she was coming here to work too."

"I'm glad this is my day off, so I could meet you," said Tommie. "We'll see Rita at lunch."

"Rita!" exclaimed Elise and Tina together. "You mean Rita's here too?"

Tommie laughed for pure joy. "Yes, she arrived day before yesterday. Just think, four of us together on our first real nursing job after graduation! After I'd worked here a week the doctor asked me if I knew of anyone else who might be interested in coming to work. I gave him your names, and Rita's. As far as I knew, the rest of the girls had jobs. I hoped he could persuade one of you to come, but to have all three of you here, why, it will be like old times!"

"Do you live in the nurses' home, Tommie?" asked Tina.

"Yes. And do you know what? We are going to have a little apartment of our own there—two bedrooms and a sitting room."

"When the doctor called me, he said the hospital was desperately short of nurses," commented Elise.

"There's an epidemic of polio here now," said Tommie. "I had to learn about it in a hurry, because most of the nurse's aides knew more about it than I did. Everybody helps you learn, though."

"Do you have any trouble with your meals? I mean, do they serve pork and meat?" queried Elise.

"No trouble at all," Tommie replied. "Mrs. Mason—that's the superintendent of nurses—took her training in an Adventist hospital although she isn't an Adventist. The doctor in charge is an Adventist, and he has arranged with the kitchen to serve us vegetarian meals."

"Are you taking any classes at the college?" asked Elise.

"No. I got here too late to start the first semester," was Tommie's answer. "I may take a few classes next semester if this epidemic slows down. I'm afraid we can't be spared until it is over."

"What about Sabbaths?" questioned Tina.

"So far I've had every Sabbath off," Tommie replied. "The anesthetist, the night supervisor, and one of the floor nurses are Adventists, and I suppose that if many more Adventists are added to the staff some of us will have to work an occasional Sabbath. However, I know Mrs. Mason will do all she can to keep our Sabbath work to a minimum. I mentioned, I think, that she trained in one of our hospitals. You'll like her."

"Is this the hospital?" asked Elise as the taxi came to a stop in front of a brick building.

"No, this is the nurses' home," said Tommie. "Doesn't it look homelike, with the porch across the front, and the flower boxes? Let's hurry and get your things put away. Then we'll go to lunch, and after that I'll take you on a tour of the hospital."

Tommie stood in front of the mirror and adjusted her cap. Tina watched idly from where she was curled on the bed.

"Aren't you going to get dressed today?" Tommie teased. "You surely are lazy on your day off!"

"You're just jealous of my pretty housecoat, Tommie," replied Tina with a grin. "Yes, to tell the truth, I'm going to get dressed pretty soon now. When Elise and Rita get off duty we are all going out to Bartons' for the afternoon and for supper."

"Well, while you're having a good time, think of me slaving away on the polio wards," smiled Tommie. "It's visiting day, you know!"

"Huh! What do you mean, 'slaving'? You love every minute of this job, even visiting day, and you know it!" retorted Tina.

"That's what I get for having a classmate for a roommate—she knows me too well! I can't even grumble and get by with it. Well, I'm going now. See you in the morning, Tina," and Tommie slipped on her coat and went out the door.

Sundays were always chaotic, Tommie reflected as she crossed the courtyard to the hospital. It was the one day in the week that the children could have visitors, and they were always impatient before their parents came, excited while they were there, and tearful after they had gone. Even as she climbed the steps to the polio wards she could hear the hubbub and clamor as parents and children made the most of visiting hours.

The nurse she was relieving gave Tommie a quick report on the children, flashed a grin, and said, "Well, it's all yours. Good luck—you're going to need it!" and was gone. The first minor crisis came almost immediately.

"Miss Gordon!" It was Miss Camp, the aide. "Joannie is crying her heart out, and I can't do a thing with her. Would you come and see what is wrong?"

Joannie had buried her face in her pillow, and her small shoulders were shaking with sobs.

"What's wrong, Joannie?" Tommie asked as she placed a gentle hand on the little girl's back.

Joannie turned slightly so one tear-filled eye peeked up at Tommie, and then she cried, "Oh, Miss Gordon, my mother didn't come today! The only day in the whole week she could come, and she didn't come at all! She doesn't love me anymore!"

Tommie remembered that Joannie's mother was a widow with three smaller children, and besides, she was dependent upon the city bus for transportation.

"Joannie, listen to me," said Tommie. "Your mother probably missed her bus or the baby-sitter couldn't come at the last minute. You wait—she'll be here before long. Visiting hours aren't over yet."

"No, she won't! No, she won't!" interrupted the little girl wildly. "She doesn't love me anymore because I'm going to be crippled!"

"Miss Camp," Tommie turned to the aide at her side, "will you go to the kitchen and get me a cereal bowl?" The aide looked surprised but hurried away, and Tommie smoothed Joannie's hair until Miss Camp returned.

With a thank-you to Miss Camp, Tommie turned to the little girl, saying firmly, "Now, Joannie, if you are going to cry, I don't see any reason to waste all those good salty tears. You catch them in this bowl, and when you get it full I'll go to town and get a goldfish to put in there!"

Joannie caught her breath in surprise and began to laugh in spite of herself. "Oh, Miss Gordon, you're a n-n-nut!" She was still laughing when her mother hurried in, explaining apologetically that the baby-sitter had been late and caused her to miss the bus. Joannie hurled herself into her mother's arms, laughing and crying at the same time, and as Tommie walked away she had a glimpse of the bewildered mother's face as Joannie incoherently tried to explain something about goldfish and cereal bowls.

Tommie continued her rounds to visit each child and tried to remember some little incident to tell each parent about his child, for she knew they desperately missed their youngsters and looked forward to these Sunday visiting hours. Some parents drove more than seven hundred miles round trip to spend a few hours with their children.

Not all children had visitors, though. In one four-bed ward she noticed that three of the little boys had visitors, as usual, but the fourth one, little Roger, hadn't had a visitor since Tommie had come to work at the hospital almost three months before. Tommie and Chad had taken the little fellow to the zoo the previous afternoon, the first time he'd been outside in months, and he had been wide-eyed and speechless with delight. Now, as she stood by his bed, he plucked at her uniform and said shyly, "We went to the zoos yesterday, didn't we?"

Tommie gave him a hug as she answered, "We certainly did, and we'll go again, you wait and see!"

As she left the room, she heard him say proudly to the others in the room, "Yesterday Miss Gordon took me to the zoos, and we're going to go again someday! She said so!"

In the hall stood three iron lungs, two of them in action, their "sigh—hiss—sigh—hiss" mingling with the other noises of the ward. Tommie stopped to talk to the parents of the two boys, Lonnie and Roy, who were in the two operating respirators. She had saved her favorite patient for the last.

Barbie! Tommie wondered if there had ever been another child like her. Barbie was twelve, and she had been in the respirator for several months. She was almost totally paralyzed. However, she had improved, and every day for longer and longer periods she had been able to have the respirator turned off. Barbie never lost her bright smile, even during the time she had been acutely ill, and she was a general favorite. Hospital workers from other departments made it a practice to come by and talk to her, and on Sundays the parents of the other children stopped to have a word with the sunny-natured little girl. Barbie's younger brother, Jerry, was in the boys' ward, also a polio victim, but his condition was better than hers.

Before long visiting hours were over. Tommie spent some time comforting the children who cried when their parents left, then supper was served and cleared away, and the next time Tommie looked at her watch she was surprised to see that it was past seven o'clock. She took one last look through the wards before starting work on the charts. The parents of one little boy had brought him an electric train that day, and the big boys were helping him run it, while the smaller boys watched in fascination. The little girls were happy with paper dolls, and the older girls were chatting quietly. Seeing that all was peaceful, Tommie sat down at her desk to do the paper work that was required of each shift.

"Miss Gordon!"

Tommie looked up to see Von's head peering around the door of the treatment room where he had secreted himself to write letters.

"Yes, Von. What is it?"

"How do you spell 'address'?"

"A-d-d-r-e-s-s."

"Two d's?"

"Yes, Von."

"Oh! Thank you!"

Tommie worked away at the charts for a while, and then she was aware of small fingers running softly across the back of her uniform. Turning, she found little red-haired Manny smiling shyly at her. Putting her arms around him, she asked, "Manny, are you my good boy?" He nodded without speaking, and then, still smiling, skipped up the hall to join the group around the train. Tommie continued her work.

In a little while it was Rene at the desk wanting attention. "Take my t'utches, p'ease, Miss Go'don," the wee mite demanded. Three-year-old Rene was a veteran at managing crutches but had a much harder time managing certain sounds in speech. Tommie took the tiny crutches and placed them on the desk, and then lifted the little girl into the chair at her side.

"Now, young lady, what can I do for you?" asked Tommie.

"W'ite me a picture, p'ease, Miss Go'don!"

"All right, but what kind of picture do you want?"

"A house picture!" So Tommie drew a picture of a house, with a boy and a girl and a dog for good measure, and Rene was delighted. Collecting her crutches, she went off down the hall to the ward with the precious picture clutched in one tiny hand.

"Miss Gordon!" It was Von again.

"Yes, Von?"

"How do you spell 'nephew'?"

"N-e-p-h-e-w."

"Oh, thank you! I was trying to spell it with an 'f' and it didn't look right."

Tommie left the last few charts to be finished after the patients had been put to bed. She went to give the few medicines needed by her group. By nine-thirty the wards were quiet, and only the sound of the respirators could be heard. After a while Miss Camp came and sat by the desk.

"Miss Gordon," she said, "you should hear that Joannie! She says she is going to keep that cereal bowl and really put a goldfish in it when she gets home, so she will have something to remember you by!"

"The little rascal!" laughed Tommie. "That sounds like her! If she could only have seen herself!" She stood up, stretched, and said, "I need some exercise! I'll make one final round of the wards before the night nurse gets here."

At the door to the boys' ward she was arrested by slight sounds. They sounded like sobs, muffled by a pillow or blanket. Standing still to locate where they were coming from, she decided it must be Wesley. But why would Wesley be crying? Wesley was twelve; he'd had visitors that day and had seemed cheerful after they were gone.

Tommie tiptoed to the bed. "Wesley?" she whispered.

"Miss Gordon?"

"What's wrong, Wesley?"

"Oh, Miss Gordon, I don't like to be a baby and—and—cry. Only tonight some of the boys said—the boys said my mother was a witch—they said she looked like one!"

"Why, Wesley!" Wesley's mother was older than the mothers of most of the boys, and she had several unsightly growths on her face, but her love for Wesley lit up that same face so that only children in their cruelty would have mentioned her looks.

"Miss Gordon, you don't think my mother looks like a witch, do you?" Tommie knew that his face was pleading, even though it was too dark for her to see it, for it was evident in his voice.

"Of course I don't," Tommie answered. "I'll have a talk with those boys tomorrow."

"I know my mother isn't—isn't very—pretty—" The words came out painfully.

"You're wrong there, Wesley," Tommie said softly. "When she smiles at you, your mother is very pretty. All mothers are when they show their love for their children. Your mother loves you very much, and she shows it."

"Really and truly, Miss Gordon?"

"Of course, Wesley. Don't you fret about what those boys said, because you know your mother far better than they do. Now, do you want me to stay here awhile, or are you all right?"

"I'm all right, Miss Gordon. I'm sorry I was such a baby and cried; but those boys made me so mad!"

"Go to sleep, then, Wesley. I'll see you in the morning!" And Tommie tiptoed out of the ward, and back to the desk, to find the night nurse waiting for her.

Another visiting day had rolled around. As Tommie made her way through the wards, she, as usual, left her favorite little Barbie to the last. As she stopped by the respirator, she saw that the bed had been pulled partly out so that the little girl could see up and down the hall, and could better visit with her parents.

Tommie greeted Barbie's father and mother, and said, "Well, Barbie, how are you today?"

Barbie answered with her usual smile. "I'm fine, Miss Gordon. I've been out of the respirator since nine o'clock this morning."

"That's wonderful, Barbie," replied Tommie. "Keep it up, and before long you'll be down in the ward with the rest of the girls."

That evening the resident doctor came by and stopped by Barbie's respirator. "Barbie, honey," he said, "we don't want you to get tired, so I think we'd better put you back in the lung. OK with you?"

"I guess so," replied Barbie. "I've been out since nine o'clock this morning."

"You're doing fine," said the doctor as he stooped to turn on the machine.

With the respirator running it was difficult for Barbie to say more than a few words at a time, due to the rhythmic changing of pressure within the machine, but she smiled at the doctor.

When the children were put to bed, Miss Camp came again and sat by the desk. "Miss Gordon, Joannie sent you a special message. She said to tell you her mother came on time today, so she didn't have any new tears to put in the cereal bowl, and that last week's tears evaporated, so you can take the bowl back to the kitchen any time you want to!"

Tommie laughed. "Isn't she a dear? She tickles me to death!"

"Miss Gordon!" It was Barbie's voice. Barbie's respirator was still close by the desk, although she was long past the stage where she required constant watching. "Miss Gordon—you are—just a—giggle-box—and someday—I'm going—to sit by—your desk—and laugh—with you!"

"All right, Barbie. I'd love to have you sit here with me. I'll even have a special chair put here for you. Now, do you want me to comb your hair?"

Barbie liked to have her hair combed at bedtime; it seemed to soothe her. Tommie knew that the little girl got terribly tired lying in the respirator day after day, although she never complained.

This evening as she brushed Barbie's long brown hair, Tommie sang a little tune. It was a habit that had gotten her into trouble more than once during her days in nursing school. The hospital authorities had looked with disfavor upon one who seemed unable to work without humming or singing at the same time. In the children's hospital, though, no one seemed to mind, and the patients actually seemed to enjoy it when Tommie forgot her training and sang to herself as she went about her duties.

"Jesus loves me, this I know,
For the Bible tells me so.
Little ones to Him belong,
They are weak but He is strong!"

Tommie thought Barbie was asleep until she spoke. "Miss Gordon —that is a—pretty song. What is—the name—of it?"

Surprise held Tommie silent for a moment. Was it actually possible for a child in the United States to reach the age of twelve without having heard "Jesus Loves Me"? Even she had heard it all her life, although she'd had no religious training as a child.

"Why, Barbie, that is 'Jesus Loves Me.' Haven't you heard it before?"

"No," replied Barbie. "Will you—sing it—again?"

"Of course," answered Tommie. When she had finished the song the second time she asked, "Barbie, do you ever go to church?"

"No," answered the little girl. "I don't—think—so. I can't—remember—ever going!"

"Do you know about Jesus?"

"Well—He is—like God—isn't He? Do you—know any—more songs like—that one?"

"Jesus is the Son of God. He died for our sins," answered Tommie. Again she sang "Jesus Loves Me" and followed with "Jesus Loves the Little Children" and "Jesus Loves the Little Ones Like Me." She was grateful for the time she'd spent working in the kindergarten division in Sabbath School.

Just as Barbie was drifting off to sleep she spoke drowsily, "Will you—sing to me—every night—when you—comb—my hair?"

"Yes, I will, Barbie," was the reply, and Tommie made a mental note to get some copies of *Our Little Friend* next Sabbath and read the stories to Barbie at night.

"Miss Gordon," Barbie spoke again sleepily. "I almost—didn't have —any company—today. My daddy—had a—cold—but he felt—he just —couldn't bear—not to see—Jerry and—me, so he came—anyway. The doctor—said he—shouldn't have—come because—it wouldn't—be good for—me to get—a cold."

Tommie felt a chill of dread. It would indeed be bad for Barbie to get a cold. The months in the respirator had left her in a weakened condition, and a cold that a normally healthy child could throw off with ease could be dangerous, even disastrous, to Barbie.

"The doctor is right, little one. Now, go to sleep!" Shortly afterward Tommie finished her work, and at eleven o'clock went thankfully home to the nurses' residence.

The next day was quieter. In the afternoon Jerry had a small tantrum and refused to obey the aide or take his treatments. Barbie heard the aide telling Tommie about it and spoke up. "Miss Gordon, if you will bring Jerry out here on a stretcher, I'll take care of him and see that he behaves himself!"

Tommie and Miss Camp exchanged smiles. It was their opinion that when Jerry got so lonesome for Barbie that he could no longer bear it, he became disobedient and noisy until he was taken out to see her. She would scold him, and after that he would be very good for a while. Of course it was unthinkable that a boy of ten, going on eleven, would come right out and say he missed his sister and badly wanted to see her: hence Jerry's strategy.

Jerry was taken up the hall on a stretcher and left for a while near Barbie while Tommie and the aides prepared the supper trays. At suppertime he was taken back to his own bed, looking surprisingly cheerful for a boy whose sister had just given him a somewhat maternal scolding and lectured him on how to get along better in the hospital.

That night Tommie again sang to Barbie, and also on the following two nights. Barbie couldn't seem to get enough of the songs. Sometimes during the day Tommie thought she heard Barbie trying to sing the songs herself, but she couldn't be sure. Barbie was out of the respirator during the day, having the machine on only at night.

Thursday night Barbie was fretful for the first time since Tommie had known her. "I don't feel good, Miss Gordon. I just don't feel good!"

"Tell me, Barbie—do you hurt? Where are you sick?"

"I don't know. I just don't feel good," the little girl repeated. Tommie put her back in the respirator so she wouldn't get too tired, and watched her carefully. There seemed to be no sign of a cold, but Tommie was worried.

The resident doctor came by several times to check on the little girl. The last time he came Tommie was brushing Barbie's hair and singing the songs Barbie requested.

Taking Tommie aside he said in a low voice, "I don't like this. I surely hope she hasn't caught cold. I noticed her temperature was up one degree." He looked at the chart. "Yes, one degree. Watch that carefully, will you? And do anything you can to keep her quiet and happy."

When Tommie went off duty that night, Barbie's temperature had gone up another four tenths of a degree, and her face was flushed. Tommie prayed earnestly for the little girl, and even then she found it hard to sleep.

The next morning Tommie hurried to the hospital. She was to work the morning shift that day. Her heart sank as she entered the polio wards and noticed the knot of people around Barbie's respirator —the head doctor, the resident doctor, a lab technician, the head nurse, and an aide. It had happened! Barbie had a cold, and her condition was not good.

Barbie smiled but did not speak when Tommie joined the group. Her face was flushed and her eyes bright with fever. Tommie assigned the morning's work to the aides and stationed herself by Barbie. In a few minutes the head nurse turned to her and said, "Miss Gordon, I'll give you the rest of this shift off. The night nurse is unable to be here tonight, and I want you to work in her place. Run on now, and get some more sleep if you can. I think," glancing toward the respirator, "that it is going to be a hard night!"

Tommie went, reluctantly, for she would gladly have stayed with Barbie the clock around, but she realized that without sleep she could not adequately care for the child. The crisis was most likely to come during the night, and she wanted to be there and see it through with the little one she loved. Her whole heart was in the polio ward, fighting the battle along with Barbie. Over and over she prayed for the little girl, until finally she went to sleep. At three o'clock she awakened when Tina came in after the morning shift. Tommie sat up.

"Barbie?" She asked the question in one word.

"Barbie is in a coma," Tina replied. "They aren't too hopeful."

Tommie napped restlessly during the rest of the afternoon, trying to sleep, for she needed to be alert and watchful when she went to work. Finally she got dressed and went to the floor an hour early. During this night she would be responsible for the whole hospital, so she made the rounds of each floor when the night nurses came on duty at eleven o'clock, telling them that she would be on the polio wards most of the night and that they could find her there.

Barbie's parents had been called, and when they came Barbie did not appear to know them. They were now in an empty room nearby, exhausted by worry and by their three-hundred-mile drive to the hospital. Jerry had not been told of his sister's condition.

The hours crept by. There wasn't much to do but just stay beside Barbie. Now and then Tommie sponged the hot little face with a cool washcloth, and smoothed back the long hair. She prayed, long and earnestly, during those hours. But Barbie never moved. The nurses and aides from other floors came on one pretext or another, and would stand and look sorrowfully at Barbie, sometimes with tear-filled eyes.

At four in the morning, when Tommie took Barbie's temperature, she saw it was not as high as it had been. Then about twenty minutes later Barbie opened her eyes and asked weakly, "May I have a drink?"

"Of course you may, Barbie," Tommie answered, her heart hammering hard from pure joy. Surely now the crisis was past!

Barbie drank the cold fruit juice Tommie brought her. Then she asked, "Will you sing for me?"

Tommie's voice wasn't quite steady as she sang Barbie's favorite, "Jesus Loves Me." When she had finished Barbie asked, "Didn't my mother and daddy come and see me during the night?"

"Yes, they are here," answered Tommie. "I'll go and get them."

"Are they asleep?" asked the little girl.

"Yes, they are right now," replied Tommie.

"Then don't get them," requested Barbie. "They must be tired after driving here. Let them sleep."

"Isn't that just like our Barbie," thought Tommie, "to consider others before herself, even as sick as she is?" But she said to the child, "Your parents asked to be called as soon as you were awake, so I'll go and get them." As she went she sent a grateful prayer of thanks heavenward.

Barbie's parents stayed with her only a few minutes, as they did not want her to become tired from talking to them. Soon after they left, the resident doctor came by to see the patient. Her temperature was still going down, and she was taking fluids freely.

"Doctor, she's going to be all right, isn't she? Isn't the crisis past? Surely she's going to be all right now!" Tommie felt happy enough to fly because Barbie seemed so much better. Oh, the Lord had been good to answer the prayers that had been presented on Barbie's behalf, so good to spare the sunny-natured child who was loved by everyone, and to give Tommie another chance to tell Barbie of the love of Jesus for her.

The doctor looked at Tommie sympathetically; he knew how much Barbie meant to her. "I'm afraid she's not yet out of danger," he said slowly, "but if her heart holds out for the next twenty-four hours, we'll have a good chance to pull her through."

But Tommie didn't share the doctor's caution. Surely the Lord had heard her prayers and would spare Barbie. She went to the nurses' residence with a happy heart, and after thanking the Lord for His goodness, she slept soundly.

Rita came in shortly after three o'clock and closed the door softly, but Tommie roused. "How is Barbie?" she asked sleepily.

Rita delayed her answer so long that Tommie sat up and saw with surprise that her roommate was crying. Fear stabbed at Tommie's heart. "Oh, surely Barbie isn't—"

"Barbie's gone," Rita finally managed to say. "She died this afternoon about two!"

Good-bye, Tommie Gordon | 21

"I have a letter from Anne," Tommie announced as she entered the apartment.

"What does she say?" asked Rita.

"She's going to be married next month, and she wants me to be maid of honor."

"Who is the lucky young man? An Adventist, I hope?" said Elise.

"Yes, he is," Tommie answered Elise's last question first. "His name is Dan Wilding. I'm so happy for her."

"So am I," said Tina. "Are you going to the wedding, Tommie?"

"Yes," Tommie answered. "I've already talked to Mrs. Mason, and she has given me five days off. And since I'm to be Anne's only attendant, I can choose my own dress."

"And you'll get a green one," teased Rita.

"No, Anne says it has to be pink," replied Tommie. "Let's go to town tomorrow and see if we can find one for me."

"I can't go," said Rita. "I have a class at the college in the morning, and I work all afternoon."

"You and I aren't on the same shift tomorrow, Tommie," said Elise, "but while you are downtown, why don't you pick out a nice wedding gift for Anne and we'll all help pay for it."

"All right," agreed Tommie. "I can take it to her when I go to the wedding."

"Maybe you'd better have the store send it to her," suggested Elise. "Something may happen to prevent your going."

"Oh, I hope not," said Tommie, "but I'll do as you say. Can you go with me, Tina?"

"Yes, I think so."

"Good! Any ideas as to what we might get for Anne?"

"How about a nice wool blanket?" suggested Rita.

"All right, we'll look for a blanket," said Tina.

142

"Don't let Tommie pick it out," teased Rita. "She would surely pick green." Everyone was aware of Tommie's favorite color.

"No, sir! I wouldn't, either! Red! This is for Anne, and Anne likes red!" Tommie exclaimed a bit heatedly.

"We'll remember to get green things when we shop for Tommie's wedding gift," smiled Elise.

"Let's get Anne's first," laughed Tommie. "After all, my wedding isn't until June first, over three months away."

"When is your cousin Val getting married?" asked Tina.

"He and Beth are being married on June third, two days after Chad and I," replied Tommie. "Beth is making her own wedding dress, but then she's a home ec. major. She is such a nice girl. She's going to lend me her veil for my 'something borrowed.'"

"When are you going to shop for your wedding dress, Tommie?" asked Elise.

"I look around every time I go to town. One of these days I'm going to find the one I want!" Tommie replied.

"I'll help you look tomorrow," offered Tina.

"All right, but first I'll need the dress for Anne's wedding."

"There, now!" said Tommie, shutting the lid to her suitcase with a thump. "I'm packed and ready to leave as soon as I get off duty tomorrow."

"Give Anne our love," requested Elise.

"I will," said Tommie. "I wish we could all go."

"So do we, but the hospital can spare only one of us at a time," said Tina.

Tommie yawned. "I'm going to bed," she announced. "I'm really tired tonight, for some reason. Good night, everybody!"

"Tommie, Tommie! What's wrong?" Rita placed her hand on Tommie's shoulder and drew it back instantly. "Why, Tommie, you're burning up with fever!"

"I th-th-think I'm h-h-having a ch-chill," Tommie replied through chattering teeth.

"Here, take this thermometer in your mouth, and I'll see if I can find some extra blankets," said Rita. "I heard your bed shaking and wondered if you were sick."

When Rita took the thermometer out of Tommie's mouth a few minutes later she exclaimed, "One hundred and four! You *are* sick!"

"My head aches, and I have a sore throat," Tommie said.

"We'd better get you over to the hospital," Rita decided.

"What time is it?" Tommie asked.

"About a quarter to five," Rita answered.

"I'll stay here in bed until the day shift comes on," said Tommie.

"All right," replied Rita. "I'll give you a couple of aspirins to bring down that temperature."

Later that morning after Tommie had been put to bed in the hospital, Dr. James came in to examine her. Rita was with him.

"How do you feel?" he asked.

"Not very well," Tommie muttered drowsily.

"Where do you hurt?"

"Throat. Abdomen."

The doctor's hands probed gently. "Ohhh, that hurts," Tommie moaned as he touched the right lower quarter of her abdomen.

"We can't do anything about this abdomen until the throat clears up or her temperature goes down," Dr. James said to Rita. "Put an ice bag over the appendix and I'll give you further orders at the desk."

"Rita?"

"Yes, Tommie?"

"Let Anne know!"

"I will. Now don't worry about it."

The next evening Tommie lay quietly in bed, sore throat gone, temperature down, and a snug binder across her abdomen where her appendix had been removed. Right at this moment she should have been in Colorado, being maid of honor at Anne's wedding. It didn't do any good to worry because it couldn't be helped.

This was a new experience, being the patient instead of the nurse.

"I don't like this; I'd much rather be up working, except I'm so sleepy," she thought, still feeling the effects of the sedatives she'd been given.

She awakened when the evening nurse entered the room. "Flowers for you, Miss Gordon," she said.

The bouquet of sweet peas was from her roommates, and the big pot of daffodils was from Chad. She had once told him how she loved daffodils, and here was proof that he remembered.

"You have visitors outside too," the nurse went on. "They can only stay a few minutes."

Val and Beth stayed only long enough to ask how she was feeling, and then Chad came. He stayed until visiting hours were over, promising to return the next day.

It was a relief to Tommie to return to work two weeks later. "I don't like being a patient," she explained to Rita. "It makes one feel so helpless!"

"Now that you know how your patients feel, you ought to be a better nurse," Rita reminded her.

"I hope so," answered Tommie. "I should get something out of this besides an appendectomy scar!"

It was the last day of May. Tommie was busy with a thousand things, but she got to the phone outside her door before it could ring a second time.

"Miss Gordon, you have guests in the lobby!"

Tommie fairly flew down the steps, and Anne caught her as she reached the bottom. "How are you, Roomie?" Anne asked, throwing her arms around Tommie.

"Fine," bubbled Tommie. "I'm so glad you're here."

"This is my husband Dan, Tommie," Anne said, indicating the tall, tanned young man at her side. "Dan, this is Tommie."

"You're the young lady who preferred to have her appendix out rather than come to our wedding," he teased.

"I didn't," Tommie denied. "If you'd gotten married a week sooner I could have had both."

"I told Anne we should get married earlier, but she felt she had to wait," he said with a smile at his bride.

"I had to wait until I could get someone to take my place in the office," Anne explained to Tommie.

"At least you're here for my wedding tomorrow," Tommie said.

At that moment the lobby phone rang, and Tommie answered it. It was Tina.

"Tommie, Wendy is here at the hospital," she said. "I'll bring her right over."

"Anne is here too," Tommie informed her.

"Wonderful!" cried Tina. "We'll come right away. I've arranged for Wendy and her sister to have the guest room in the nurses' home."

"Fine! Now hurry!" Tommie turned to Anne. "Wendy is here now too."

"Almost a class reunion," laughed Anne.

The rest of the afternoon was spent catching up on class news.

Over one third of the class were present, and the names of the others came up constantly in conversation.

"What time is it?" "We're due at the church at one o'clock!" "Tommie, you haven't begun to get dressed."

Tommie laughed at the commotion around her. "It won't take me more than half an hour to dress," she said, "and it won't take half an hour to drive to the church, although I've allowed that much time for it. So don't worry. We'll get there on time."

"I don't believe you're a bit nervous, Tommie," Elise observed.

"No butterflies as big as eagles in your stomach?" Anne queried.

"No last-minute regrets?" teased Wendy.

"Remember what I said once about romances by mail and you indignantly denied that your correspondence with Chad would develop into any such thing?" asked Tina with a sly smile.

"I was wrong, and I'm glad to admit it," Tommie confessed promptly.

"It takes real courage to admit you're wrong," teased Tina.

Tommie took a deep breath. "Not when it turns out as perfectly as this has," she said happily.

"The taxi's here, girls," called Elise. "Tommie, hold up your skirt coming down the stairs."

"I have the sheet to put over the seat of the taxi," said Rita.

"I have the veil, and the comb to redo your hair when we get to the church, Tommie," added Wendy.

"I'm glad the rain let up for a few minutes," said Tina.

Shortly after the girls arrived at the church, Tommie was ready.

"There, now! Your hair is fixed. Let me put your veil on you," said Wendy. "And here's your bouquet."

"There's the music beginning," whispered Tommie. She peeked through the back door up to the front of the church. Chad, the best man, and the minister were already in place. Elise was sitting where Mamma would have been if Daddy had let her come to the wedding.

"Tommie!" scolded Tina. "You aren't supposed to peek!"

"I always peek," said Tommie. "I'm just naturally curious to see how things are going." Suddenly she began to giggle.

Tina raised an inquiring eyebrow, and looked at Rita. "Hysteria?" she asked cryptically.

"Of course not," laughed Tommie. "I just happened to think of

146

what Lucille said the night of graduation about getting married to 'Pomp and Circumstances' instead of a wedding march."

"Tommie's all right," said Rita. "It's time for us to go. You first, Tina."

"Here's my arm, Tommie," said Val. "As your only relative present, I count it a privilege to escort you up the aisle."

"Thank you, Val."

"Here Comes the Bride," announced the organ.

Tommie and Val came through the door. Tommie's glance met Chad's, and they both smiled.